Chemistry, 2nd Edition Workbook

Frank Cardulla, M.A.

THE
GREAT
COURSES

PUBLISHED BY:

THE GREAT COURSES
Corporate Headquarters
4840 Westfields Boulevard, Suite 500
Chantilly, Virginia 20151-2299
Phone: 1-800-832-2412
Fax: 703-378-3819
www.thegreatcourses.com

Frank Cardulla, M.A.

Niles North High School

Describing himself as "a retired teacher who can't seem to stay retired," Professor Frank Cardulla is a veteran of 38 years of public high school teaching—35 of them at Niles North High School in Skokie, Illinois, a suburb of Chicago. He holds a B.S. in the Teaching of Chemistry and an M.A. in the Teaching of Physical Sciences, both from the University of Illinois at Urbana-Champaign, as well as 60 credit hours of postgraduate education at various institutions.

During his tenure, Professor Cardulla has taught chemistry at every high school academic level. His primary assignments were to the first-year honors and second-year Advanced Placement courses at Niles North, where his students established a legacy filled with a long list of academic awards and scholarships in various competitions. Two former students worked closely with 2 Nobel Prize winners on the research for which their prizes were awarded. He has received citations from institutions such as MIT and the University of Chicago for being named "most influential teacher" by attending students.

Average and struggling students have always held a special place in Professor Cardulla's heart. Much of his time, effort, and thought has been directed toward developing an approach to solving introductory chemistry problems that will allow the average student to succeed. He helps students realize that what often seems a difficult subject is in reality a simple subject that utilizes the natural quantitative reasoning abilities that they possess.

At every opportunity, Professor Cardulla has enthusiastically jumped at the chance to teach courses outside of the honors track. These courses have included regular-level traditional chemistry, Chemistry for the Health Sciences, and Chemistry in the Community. In addition, he has served as science seminar director, taught physics, and on one occasion taught a special education class of 6 students, something he still calls "the most inspiring, enjoyable, and rewarding teaching experience I ever had." He has also served as an Adjunct Professor at Northwestern University in Evanston, Illinois, teaching a science methods course for several years.

Throughout his career, Professor Cardulla has been very active in helping to prepare numerous national chemistry examinations, serving on and chairing several American Chemical Society examinations committees that prepared examinations for both regular and Advanced Placement high school courses as well as the Chemistry in the Community Course and the first Conceptual Chemistry examination. In addition, he served as a member of the Advanced Placement Chemistry Test Development Committee that prepared 3 of the College Board's Advanced Placement chemistry examinations.

Professor Cardulla has delivered more than 30 presentations on a wide variety of topics, including several devoted to his approach to teaching problem solving that is utilized in this lecture series. Some notable titles include "Acid-Base Chemistry," "History and Development of Modern Atomic Theory," "Thermodynamics," "Problem Solving," "De Broglie's Hypothesis and the Heisenberg Uncertainty Principle," "The Life and Work of Louis de Broglie," "Teaching Schrodinger's Equation to High School Sophomores," and "Teaching High School Chemistry Without Utilizing the Factor-Label Method."

Professor Cardulla has published several articles in the *Journal of Chemical Education* and *ChemMatters* magazine; he also served as a reviewer for the latter publication and as associate editor for an outreach program connected with NASA's Aura project to study Earth's atmosphere.

Professor Cardulla's contributions to chemical education have been recognized with numerous teaching awards, the most notable being a Presidential Award in Mathematics and Science Teaching, the National Catalyst Award, and the National James Bryant Conant Award. The last 2 are given to only 1 high school chemistry teacher in the nation each year.

Table of Contents
Chemistry, 2nd Edition

Table of Contents
Chemistry, 2nd Edition

Workbook Answers

Chemistry, 2nd Edition

Scope:

High school chemistry, unfortunately, is a subject that too often is either (1) avoided by many high school students whenever possible, (2) taken only because of college admission requirements, or (3) described later in life as "my worst subject."

This all-too-common view is the dragon that this course attempts to slay.

The central tenet permeating all 36 lectures is that learning based on true understanding stands a higher chance of success in the long run. Rote memorization may succeed in the short term or be useful for learning a few basic concepts, but true understanding increases the likelihood of success as more concepts are added each lecture.

The first lecture expounds this philosophy, followed by hopefully convincing demonstrations that solving most high school chemistry problems does not require any special talent or intellectual ability. The vast majority of high school students possess more than adequate mental equipment to succeed admirably, and they use naturally and easily in their daily lives the same kind of quantitative reasoning ability that is used to solve high school chemistry problems.

Lectures Two and Three demonstrate how a student's logical thinking skills can be used to perform basic calculations that are common throughout the course. We then discuss popular problem-solving techniques, emphasizing logical thinking instead of rote memorization of procedures or rules. We apply these quantitative reasoning skills to the simple concept of density in Lecture Four.

Lecture Five follows with a discussion of that stalwart topic in high school chemistry courses—the International System of Units (SI), or the metric system. After a brief discussion of its history and advantages, we address SI basic and derived units, along with the metric prefixes encountered throughout the course. In Lecture Six we use this information to convert between SI and non-SI units.

The next 3 lectures are devoted to preliminary ideas valuable both in and of themselves and containing information useful in later lessons. Lecture Seven explores the development of the periodic table, including a discussion of the elements. We then extend this discussion to include ions, chemical formulas, protons, electrons, and atomic weights in Lecture Eight. Lecture Nine concludes this preliminary overview with a discussion of isotopes, neutrons, and mass numbers, along with a general summary of the periodic table's structure.

Lecture Ten addresses the key topic permeating most high school problems—the mole. We explore the importance of this concept and its relationship to molar masses and Avogadro's number. We use these relationships to solve sample mole-related problems in Lecture Eleven. In Lecture Twelve we examine the relationship between the mole and the molar volume of gases and apply these ideas to sample problems.

Lecture Thirteen demonstrates how the mole concept can be applied to determine the percent composition of each element in a compound. We then use percent compositions and other laboratory data to determine empirical and molecular formulas in Lecture Fourteen.

After learning how to write and balance chemical equations in Lecture Fifteen, the next 3 lectures cover what is often the core topic that frustrates students—stoichiometry. Lecture Sixteen demonstrates how a balanced equation serves as a chemical "recipe" and explores the important role of the mole in stoichiometry. Lectures Seventeen and Eighteen expand on these basic concepts as we solve a variety of typical stoichiometry problems.

The next 3 lectures examine the concentrations of solutions. Lecture Nineteen introduces the most common unit of measurement for concentration—molarity—and demonstrates how to prepare a solution correctly. We will apply these basic concepts to solve various molarity problems in Lectures Twenty and Twenty-One.

We spend the next 3 lectures discussing the fundamental concepts of equilibrium, with an emphasis on understanding as opposed to just memorizing. Lecture Twenty-Two addresses the basic ideas related to chemical equilibrium, and Lectures Twenty-Three and Twenty-Four explore these ideas quantitatively by using the equilibrium constant. Qualitative changes in equilibrium systems are treated by applying Le Chatelier's principle, as we see in Lectures Twenty-Five and Twenty-Six.

With this firm foundation established, Lecture Twenty-Seven tackles various types of equilibrium problems. We then discuss the self-ionization of water and pH in Lecture Twenty-Eight. We continue the discussion of pH in Lectures Twenty-Nine and Thirty as we describe the characteristics of strong acids and bases. In Lecture Thirty-One, we compare the characteristics of strong and weak acids and bases and solve related equilibrium and pH problems.

Lectures Thirty-Two and Thirty-Three introduce a common laboratory technique used to determine unknown concentrations of acids and bases—the titration. In Lecture Thirty-Three, we also discuss the chemistry behind acid-base indicators that are used during titrations.

We move on to qualitative and quantitative discussions of solubility in Lectures Thirty-Four and Thirty-Five. Lecture Thirty-Four qualitatively discusses solubility and then quantitatively defines it by using the solubility product constant. In Lecture Thirty-Five, we examine the common ion effect and discuss its impact on solubility equilibrium.

This lecture series concludes with a capstone lecture called "Putting it All Together," which allows us an opportunity to pull concepts from multiple lectures to try to solve a few rather demanding problems. Lecture Thirty-Six highlights the importance of understanding, instead of memorizing, the concepts presented in these lectures.

How to Use This Workbook

The questions and problems presented in this workbook are designed to provide you with both an opportunity to practice the tasks presented in the lectures and feedback on how well you are achieving the goals of both the individual lectures and the entire course.

Levels of Difficulty: For many (but not all) of the lectures, questions and problems have been divided into 2 categories, labeled standard and advanced. While these designations should not be taken too literally, in general, standard items are items it is assumed students would be expected to master in most high school courses with relatively strong academic expectations. Advanced items represent more challenging versions of classic problems and/or questions or problems that might only be addressed in what are often labeled honors courses. In some cases, questions and problems have been included that are exceptionally challenging, just for fun, and on occasion a few truly fun items have been included for no other reason than the fact that I enjoy a bit of humor now and then and thought you might also.

If you have difficulty with the advanced items, in no way should this be taken as an indication that you have not achieved adequate mastery of the material presented in the lectures.

Even standard items vary significantly in their level of difficulty. Only you can judge the academic level of achievement that is most appropriate for your particular situation and goals.

Work all Problems: My recommendation would be to try to work problems at all levels, even if they might not be demanded in your particular situation. Think of it this way: If you wanted to become an excellent miler on the track team, you would not practice by only running a mile. You would run greater, more difficult distances. A similar concept may apply here.

Worked-out solutions have been provided for all problems. Space limitations do not allow detailed written explanations of all the logic behind each solution, but I have tried to include comments to help explain the thinking that underlies each mathematical solution.

When comparing your answer to the answer given for a mathematical problem, remember that answers will often vary slightly depending on how and where numbers are rounded off during the solving process. Do not be concerned if you obtained an answer of perhaps 7.35, for example, while the answer given was 7.33, 7.37, or something similar. In addition, the number of digits or decimal places contained in the answer is not important, within reason. No serious effort has been made to observe what are often called significant figure rules, so if you wrote down your answer with either an extra digit or decimal place or perhaps one fewer digits or decimal places, this is of no significance. What is important is whether you put the numbers given in the problem together in the proper way, not how you wrote down your final answer.

Working these practice problems and/or similar items from your current text is vital for almost all students who expect to achieve proficiency at solving the kinds of problems encountered in high school chemistry. Solving problems is generally time well spent.

Contact Information: I have given a lot of thought to including my e-mail address in this introduction. I greatly enjoy receiving and responding to e-mails from students and have been able to reply to every one that I have received to date. My fear, however, is that the number might very well become so great that replying to all of them would no longer be possible at a practical level, so please be understanding if you send an e-mail and do not receive a reply. I will try very hard to respond if at all possible. My e-mail address is chemtchur@aol.com. I especially welcome your feedback as to what you found valuable and what you may have found less than optimal in both the lectures themselves and this workbook.

I wish you success in all your studies and in life.

Lecture One
Introduction and Philosophy

Scope:

This lecture sets forth the general philosophy of the course—namely, that learning is much more effective when it occurs through understanding rather than rote memorization. Though chemistry is often considered a hard course, the vast majority of high school students possess more than adequate mental equipment to succeed admirably, and they use the same kind of quantitative reasoning ability naturally and easily in their daily lives that is used to solve high school chemistry problems.

Outline

I. General introduction.

    A. Your instructor is a high school teacher with long and varied experience teaching all levels of high school chemistry.

    B. The focus of the lectures will be the general area of problem solving.

II. The major goal of these lectures is to help beginning or struggling chemistry students.

    A. Usefulness was always put before sheer entertainment value when choosing topics for inclusion.

    B. The entire focus is to increase understanding, rather than encourage memorization.

III. Approaches to problem solving based solely on memorization are almost certainly doomed to failure.

    A. Problem solving must be accompanied by understanding to ensure long-term success.

    B. The type of logical reasoning abilities required to solve introductory high school chemistry problems is very similar to what students use easily and naturally in their everyday lives.

IV. "Chemistry is the easiest class in school."

    A. Most students do not agree with the above statement and believe chemistry is, by its very nature, a difficult subject.

        1. This belief often becomes a self-fulfilling prophesy.

        2. Almost any high school student has more than adequate abilities to do well in high school chemistry.

    B. If you can work the simple problems involving students and rooms shown in this lecture, you can work virtually any chemistry problem you might be assigned.

V. Some of these lectures should probably be watched in order, but most can be watched in any sequence that is most useful to an individual student.

Lecture One—Questions
Introduction and Philosophy

1. Which statement below best describes the goals and philosophy of this course?

    A. Try and solve as many different problems as possible so you will have direct experience with every possible kind of problem you might encounter.

    B. Solve only a very few kinds of problems, since students typically do not find this aspect of high school chemistry too difficult.

    C. Learn specific formulas and approaches for as many different kinds of problems as possible, so you can have a specific approach custom designed for each problem that you might be asked to solve.

    D. Try and develop a deep understanding of fundamental concepts and modes of quantitative reasoning that can be applied to the vast majority of problems that you might be asked to solve.

2. True or false: Although high school chemistry is not that difficult a subject, it does demand that you learn and apply modes of quantitative reasoning and specific mathematical techniques that are essentially and uniquely required to solve chemistry problems. Explain.

3. What is a self-fulfilling prophesy? Give an example. How does it apply to why some students have difficulty with high school chemistry?

4. What was the point of working the students and rooms problem?

5. It is argued in these lectures that the kind of quantitative thinking used to solve most high school chemistry problems is identical to the thinking students use easily and naturally in their everyday lives. Yet it is also admitted that many students who can apply quantitative reasoning in their everyday lives still have difficulty solving chemistry problems. What 2 reasons account for this apparent contradiction?

6. Must all the lectures be viewed in order? What recommendations are made regarding the order of viewing?

7. What should you do if you are watching one of the later lectures in this course and encounter a concept or topic that you either have not studied or no longer remember?

8. What is one of the most critical things you must do to get the maximum benefit from this course?

9. Just for fun, what is the rule behind the following series of numbers? 0, 1, 1, 2, 3, 5, 8, 13, 21 …

Lecture Two
Basic Concepts of Quantitative Reasoning

Scope:

This lecture establishes the basic logical framework that students will use for the remainder of the course. Chemistry requires simple quantitative reasoning that generally comes quite naturally to students. Here we break down the types of numbers involved in the study of chemistry and the 3 approaches that can be used to solve problems involving these numbers.

Outline

I. The students and rooms problem, although very simple, illustrates the exact type of quantitative reasoning that is used in solving introductory chemistry problems.

    A. Nevertheless, students often have difficulty clearly explaining how they reasoned out the answer, even though they have no difficulty whatsoever in doing the reasoning.

    B. Few students have ever taken the time to analyze what they are really doing when they perform calculations.

    C. This problem is a simple example of a "guzinta" (goes into) problem.

II. There are only 2 different kinds of numbers in most chemistry problems: "amount" and "this per that."

III. There are 3 common approaches to solving problems that involve this type of quantitative relationship.

    A. Some students use a formula or equation.

    B. Some use the proportion method.

    C. Some use the factor-label approach.

    D. The students and rooms problem could have been solved by using any of these approaches.

    E. Although any of these approaches can be used, it is not necessary to use any of these approaches to be a successful problem solver.

IV. Chemistry problems can usually be solved by an application of simple, natural ways of reasoning quantitatively.

    A. There are basically only 3 ways in which numbers are normally related to one another.

    B. In the students and rooms problem, you have 3000 students and 30 rooms. What are the 3 ways to relate these numbers?

        1. $\frac{3000}{30}$

        2. $\frac{30}{3000}$

        3. $(3000)(30)$

    C. Because you understand the quantities involved, you know instinctively that the first way is correct. This course is about developing that same kind of understanding about the numbers involved in chemistry.

Lecture Two—Questions
Basic Concepts of Quantitative Reasoning

1. What are the 2 basic kinds of numbers that typically appear in chemistry problems?

2. Classify each of the following quantities as an amount, a this per that, or neither.
   A. 5 plates/place setting
   B. 53 players/team
   C. 66.2 g
   D. 500 marbles
   E. 30 marbles/box
   F. 500 marbles/30 marbles/box
   G. 76 trombones

3. Name 3 popular techniques that can be successfully applied to solving many chemistry problems.

4. Why is it recommended that you not rely on using formulas to solve chemistry problems?

5. Since proportions and the factor-label approach can also be successfully used to solve chemistry problems, why is it recommended that you not rely on these 2 approaches?

6. When faced with a chemistry problem that you do not immediately know how to solve, what 3 things should you get into the habit of doing?

7. What is another thing you can do if you are not confident that you worked the problem correctly?

8. What is the primary reason that some chemistry students have difficulty solving chemistry problems?

Lecture Three
Quantitative Reasoning in Everyday Life

Scope:

This lecture further explores successful strategies for understanding and solving chemistry problems. The most helpful step a student can take in approaching a problem in chemistry is to understand fully what is being asked. Visualization can often help in achieving this. The lecture concludes with several practice problems designed to help the student use these strategies.

Outline

I. There are only a handful of important ideas that must be mastered for success at solving chemistry problems.

    A. You must really try to understand what is meant and represented by the numbers (with accompanying units) stated in the problem.

    B. Whenever you divide 2 numbers, understand that you are making the denominator 1, whether you actually do the division on your calculator or not.

    C. When you are presented with a problem, read the problem several times—first quickly, then slowly; stopping, thinking, and visualizing as you go along. Draw a picture of the quantities represented in the problem. Always attach proper units to all numbers, and think about what these numbers represent.

    D. The numbers in a problem are generally of 2 types: amount and this per that.

        1. An amount is a quantity that you can visualize in your mind.

        2. A this per that tells you how many of the numerator you have for 1 of the denominator.

II. Several practice problems can help us grasp the concepts stated above.

III. The problems just worked incorporated virtually all of the quantitative reasoning skills required to solve all but a handful of the chemistry problems you will likely be asked to solve in a chemistry course.

Lecture Three—Questions
Quantitative Reasoning in Everyday Life

Note: In solving numerical problems, it may turn out that your answer will differ slightly from the answer presented. This is of no consequence if you have solved the problem correctly. Read the introduction to the workbook for a more detailed discussion of this.

Standard Problems

1. What does a this per that always tell you?

2. What does a quantity like 33 mi/h tell you?

3. What does a quantity like $\frac{238 \, mi}{4.5 \, h}$ tell you?

4. A hybrid car can get 48 mi/gal. How many gallons of gas does it take to drive 1 mi?

5. If you are having difficultly visualizing the fact that a quantity like $\frac{238 \, mi}{4.5 \, h}$ is actually telling you how many miles you drive in 1 h (not 4.5), or that $\frac{1 \, gal}{48 \, mi}$ is telling you how many gallons of gas it takes to drive 1 mi (not 48), what is a little trick you can use to help you overcome this difficulty?

6. List some of the things you should get in the habit of doing when faced with a problem you are having difficulty solving.

7. A marathon runner trains, on average, by running 8.5 mi/day. How many training miles will she have run during 6 months of training? Assume an average month has 30.5 days.

8. A car traveling at 47 mi/h travels a distance of 5 mi. Given that there are 60 min in an hour and 60 s in a minute, how many seconds did it take for the car to travel the 5 mi?

9. You go to the store to purchase some turkey. Turkey costs $6.99/lb. How much turkey can you purchase if you have $11.85 to spend?

10. You plan to drive your car a distance of 825 mi. If your car gets 29.7 mi/gal and gasoline costs $4.28/gal, how much will you have to spend on gas?

Advanced Problem

11. A teacher needs M&M's candies for a simulated radioactive decay lab (there actually is such a lab—students love it for obvious reasons). There are a total of 87 students who will have to run the lab. Each student will require about 120 M&M's to run the simulation. A single M&M weighs about 0.89 g on average. How many grams of M&M's will be needed to run the lab? If M&M's came in packages that weighed 100 g (they do not), how many packages would the teacher have to purchase?

Lecture Four
Quantitative Reasoning in Chemistry—Density

Scope:

We now apply the tools that we acquired in Lectures One through Three to a basic quantitative measure in chemistry: density. We begin by defining density and exploring its properties as a relationship between mass and volume. We then solidify our understanding of density—and our skills at problem solving—by finding solutions to some simple density problems.

Outline

I. Density is often the first quantitative concept studied in a high school chemistry course.

    A. Density problems can be solved by using a formula or some other technique, such as the proportion method or the factor-label method. However, these approaches have some significant disadvantages.

    B. A much better approach is to work at really understanding what is meant by the quantities used in defining the density of something and how they are combined to produce the density unit.

II. Density involves 2 quantities and 1 relationship.

    A. The quantities are mass and volume, perhaps measured in grams and cubic centimeters.

    B. The relationship is the number of grams that are contained in 1 cm^3.

    C. To understand density, you must understand what we mean when we talk about mass, volume, and mass per volume.

        1. The mass is the amount of matter in an object, expressed in grams. (Mass is similar to, but not the same as, weight.)

        2. The volume is the amount of space an object occupies.

        3. The density of an object is the amount of its matter in a given space; in other words, density is mass per volume.

    D. Density is an excellent example of what is meant by a ratio.

III. We can solidify our understanding of the concept of density as well as develop a deeper understanding of what is involved in quantitative reasoning by working density problems.

Lecture Four—Questions
Quantitative Reasoning in Chemistry—Density

Standard Problems

1. What do we mean when we talk about the mass of an object?

2. What does the volume of an object refer to?

3. What does the density of something refer to?

4. Which kind of quantity is density?
    - **A.** It is an amount.
    - **B.** It is a this per that.
    - **C.** It is a ratio.
    - **D.** All of the above.
    - **E.** None of the above.
    - **F.** Two of the above.

5. The density of an object is 5.00 g/cm^3. What would be the density of 2.00 cm^3 of the substance?

6. Arrange the following objects in order of mass, from the lightest to the heaviest: a nickel, a dime, an orange, a small metal fork, and a liter bottle of soda.

7. What is the density of an object that occupies a volume of 7.34 cm^3 and has a mass of 6.25 g?

8. What is the mass of 8.29 cm^3 of a material that has a density of 1.44 g/cm^3?

9. Liquid mercury (chemical symbol Hg) has a density of 13.59 g/cm^3. What volume would be occupied by 9.00 g of liquid Hg?

10. An irregularly shaped metal object has a mass of 28.73 g. It is lowered into a 100-mL graduated cylinder that contains 35.2 cm^3 water. (Note that 1 cm^3 = 1 mL.) The water level rises to 44.8 cm^3. What is the density of the metal?

11. A piece of hard candy has a mass of 6.00 g. A Nerf ball has a mass of 5.55 g. Which occupies the larger volume?

Advanced Problems

12. If an object has a density of 60.0 g/cm^3 on Earth, what would its density be on the Moon, where gravitational attraction is only about $\frac{1}{6}$ of what it is on Earth?

13. The density of a red blood cell is 1.096 g/cm^3. In normal whole blood, there are about 5.40×10^9 red blood cells/cm^3. What is the volume of blood occupied by a single red blood cell?

11

Lecture Five
The SI (Metric) System of Measurement

Scope:

Lecture Five introduces a discussion of that stalwart topic in high school chemistry courses—the International System of Units (SI), or the metric system. After a brief discussion of its history and advantages, we will address the basic and derived units, along with the metric prefixes encountered throughout the course.

Outline

I. The metric system of measurement has a long historical background and grew out of a need for standard and reproducible measurements for both science and commerce.

    A. The metric system has at least 2 distinct advantages over the English system of measurement.

        1. Units are defined in terms of things that are easily and accurately reproduced.

        2. All conversions within the system can be performed by moving a decimal point.

    B. The metric system has undergone numerous minor and significant modifications over the years since its introduction.

II. In 1960, the modern SI units were established.

    A. All base units are now well defined in terms of reproducible phenomena or objects.

    B. This revision established a philosophy that declared that only a minimum number of base units would be rigorously defined; all other units would be derived from these base units.

        1. There are 7 base units.

        2. All other scientific units can be derived from combinations of these 7 base units.

        3. Because some units are not of convenient size, a few additional units remain in common use in chemistry.

III. There are 20 different SI prefixes. (You can find them all in the appendices.)

Lecture Five—Questions
The SI (Metric) System of Measurement

Standard Problems

1. Name the 5 base units of SI measurement that we will use in this course, state what they measure, and write the correct abbreviation for each unit of measurement.

2. For each of the following derived units, list the correct SI unit and some commonly used metric unit that is not actually the correct SI unit:

   A. Mass

   B. Volume

   C. Temperature

   D. Speed

3. Which 3 "large" metric prefixes are we most likely to use, and what do they represent?

4. Which 4 "small" metric prefixes are we most likely to use, and what do they represent?

5. Some metric units, like the meter, have been redefined several times. What was the purpose of doing this?

6. Which metric unit is still established by an actual physical object kept at the international bureau of standards?

Advanced Problems (Actually Just for Fun)

7. A. If you had a mockingbird that weighed 2000 g, what would you have?

   B. If you brought 1 trillion (10^{12}) bulls to a bullfight, what would that be?

   C. If you bought 1 million (10^6) phones, what would you have?

   D. If you got so mad that you smashed one of your phones into 1 million pieces, what would each piece (10^{-6} phone) be?

   E. Suppose that in some grizzly accident, a small boy was chopped into 10^{18} pieces. What would each piece be?

   F. What would you call 10 playing cards?

   G. What would you call 1 millionth (10^{-6}) of a fish?

   H. If you received 10 rations when you were in the army, what would that be?

   I. What would you call 10 millipedes?

   J. What are $\frac{30}{3}$ tridents?

8. In June 1957, *MAD Magazine* published a humorous system of weights and measures called the Potrzebie system. It was created by Donald E. Knuth, a 19-year-old student who went on to become one of the most renowned computer scientists in the world. It was a humorous, tongue-in-cheek, but completely rational and internally consistent system of measurement based on the thickness of *MAD Magazine* no. 26, listed as being 2.263348517438173216473 mm, or 1 potrzebie (1 p). Volume was measured in ngogn, mass in blintz, and density in halavah; 0.000001 p is equal to 1 farshimmelt potrzebie (1 fp); and it goes on and on. There is no assignment now except to research this system on the Internet if you wish. A fun Potrzebie problem will be included with the problems that accompany Lecture Six.

Lecture Six
Converting between Systems of Measurement

Scope:

Now that we have established an understanding of the SI, we will put that knowledge to use by converting units from one system of measurement to another. The factor-label method introduced in Lecture Two can be very useful in accomplishing these conversions. We will end by working through several practice problems to hone our conversion skills.

Outline

I. Conversion from a unit with one prefix to a unit with another can either be done by the factor-label method or by the big guy/little guy method.

    A. In the factor-label method, the quantity being converted is multiplied by a conversion factor (a fraction) with units in the appropriate place—the numerator or denominator. The starting units should cancel out, and only the desired units should remain.

    B. In the big guy/little guy approach, the size of the given quantity is compared to the desired quantity to determine how many places and in which direction the decimal point should be moved.

II. The factor-label approach to solving problems is one of the most powerful methods ever designed to obtain the answer to a simple problem.

    A. Its power lies in the fact that it is possible to obtain the correct answer without having to understand anything about the quantities involved, other than their units.

    B. Its power is also its weakness, because using this approach lets you ignore the important conceptual understandings required to do well in chemistry.

    C. Although the approach should be used cautiously, it is an excellent method for converting from one unit of measurement to another.

III. Practicing on a number of conversion problems will allow us to understand how to use the factor-label approach to do unit conversions and how to apply it to check our answers in later problems.

    A. We will begin with some fairly simple, classic types of unit conversions.

    B. We can also work conversions that involve raising units to some power.

Lecture Six—Questions
Converting between Systems of Measurement

In solving the following problems, some or all of these conversion factors may prove useful.

1 in = 2.54 cm	453.6 g = 1 lb	$1 \text{ cm}^3 = 1$ mL
12 in = 1 ft	60 s = 1 min	1.06 qt = 1 L
3 ft = 1 yd	60 min = 1 h	4 qt = 1 gal
5280 ft = 1 mi	24 h = 1 day	1.609 km = 1 mi

Standard Problems

1. Convert 3.77 mm to centimeters.

2. Convert 9.18 mm to micrometers.

3. Convert 7.93 Gmol to nanomoles.

4. Convert 5.85×10^{-7} Mg to nanograms.

5. Convert 7.22×10^6 dg to kilograms.

6. Convert 1.81 Ym to picometers.

7. How many inches are there in 167 cm?

8. How many kilograms are there in 1.33 lb?

9. How many miles are there in 1 cm?

10. How many days do you have to live to live for 1,000,000 s?

Advanced Problems

11. A 1.0×10^5-gal truck of acetone contains 6.5×10^5 lb of acetone. What is the density of acetone in grams per cubic centimeter?

12. Gold has a density of 19.0 g/cm^3. If an 18-in necklace is made of pure gold, what would be its mass, in grams, if it is 1.0 cm wide and 1.0 mm thick?

13. A satellite is orbiting Earth at 1.75×10^5 mi/h. How many seconds does it take to travel 100 mi?

14. Light travels at a speed of 3.0×10^{10} cm/s. How many nanoseconds does it take light to travel 1 cm?

15. How many miles can light travel in a year? (Use the speed of light from problem 14).

And One Just for Fun

16. In the questions that accompanied Lecture Five, problem 8 talked about a humorous system of weights and measures called the Potrzebie system. Recall that the fundamental unit of length in this system was called the potrzebie, and its standard was the thickness of *MAD Magazine* no. 26, which was said to be 2.263348517438173216473 mm, or 1 p. Volume was measured in a unit called a ngogn, which was equal to 1000 p^3. Mass was measured in blintz, and 1 blintz was equal to the mass of 1 ngogn of halavah. Halavah is a form of pie; it has a specific gravity of 3.1416, which means it is 3.1416 times as dense as liquid water. Liquid water has a density of 1 g/cm^3. What is the mass of 1 blintz of halavah, in grams? You may round off the potrzebie to 2.26335 mm.

Lecture Seven
Elements, Atoms, and the Periodic Table

Scope:

In this lecture we will explore the development of the periodic table of elements. Although there are several ways that a periodic table can be built, the example that we find in chemistry textbooks is the most common form. To understand the development and organization of the periodic table, we must also understand some basic properties of the elements themselves. The lecture ends with a discussion of the fundamental structure of all elements.

Outline

I.   There are several different ways of preparing the periodic table of elements. The most common form is found in most textbooks.

II. The periodic table displays all the known elements arranged in a pattern.

III. Elements can be defined operationally and conceptually.

    A. The operational definition of an element is "a substance that cannot be broken down into simpler substances by ordinary physical or chemical techniques."

    B. The conceptual definition of an element is "a substance made of only 1 kind of atom."

IV. By 1869, Dmitri Mendeleev had published what is generally regarded as the first true periodic table.

    A. Mendeleev's table had approximately 60 elements, compared to over 100 in the modern table.

    B. The elements were arranged according to their relative weights, from lightest to heaviest.

    C. Mendeleev and other scientists noticed that the properties of elements repeated themselves at regular intervals. Mendeleev then arranged the elements into families of elements with similar properties.

    D. Based on the properties of the elements, Mendeleev predicted the location of and some properties for several of the missing elements. These elements were later discovered and closely matched Mendeleev's predictions.

V. Each element on the periodic table is represented by a 1- or 2-letter symbol.

    A. When using 2-letter symbols, the first letter is capitalized and the second letter is lowercased.

    B. Many symbols correlate with the English name for the element. Some symbols do not because the name was derived from another language, usually Latin.

VI. Each element has a unique atomic number that represents the number of protons in the nucleus, as well as the number of electrons, in an atom of that element.

    A. A proton is a fundamental type of particle found in the nucleus of all elements, and it carries a charge of +1.

    B. Electrons are found outside the nucleus, and they carry a charge of −1.

    C. Atoms are electrically neutral, so the number of protons and electrons must be equal.

Lecture Seven—Questions
Elements, Atoms, and the Periodic Table

Standard Problems

1. What does "operational definition" mean? What might be an operational definition of a circle?

2. What does "conceptual definition" mean? What might be a conceptual definition of a circle?

3. What are the operational and conceptual definitions of an element?

4. What was one of the most daring things that Mendeleev did when he published his first periodic table?

5. While there is no master list of elements whose symbols you should commit to memory, there are several that it might be good to have memorized. What are the symbols for hydrogen, helium, lithium, carbon, nitrogen, oxygen, fluorine, neon, sodium, magnesium, aluminum, silicon, phosphorus, sulfur, chlorine, argon, potassium, calcium, chromium, iron, nickel, copper, zinc, bromine, silver, tin, iodine, xenon, barium, gold, mercury, lead, bismuth, radon, and uranium?

6. What does the atomic number of an atom tell us about the atom?

7. What is the charge of a proton?

8. What is the charge of an electron?

Advanced Problems

9. Can you find at least 1 weakness in both the operational and conceptual definitions of an element presented as the answers to question 3?

10. We say that there are only 2 different kinds of charges, which we have arbitrarily labeled as being +1 and −1. We could have just as easily called them Sammy and Joey, if we wished. We labeled them +1 and −1 because these were the only 2 different kinds of charges we found, and in addition, if we combine 1 of each of these 2 different kinds of charges, the result is no charge at all. If we assume that opposite charges attract and like charges repel, what kind of experimental result would force us to conclude that there were, in fact, 3 different kinds of charges in nature instead of only 2?

And for Fun

11. Give the symbols for each of the following elements.

    A. The undertaker's element

    B. The Lone Ranger's horse

    C. What doctors try to do with a sick person

    D. A crazy prison inmate

    E. Why the young lady wore perfume to a class where she sat next to a boy she wanted to date

    F. What torpedoed ships do

    G. What I hope you are not finding these lectures

Lecture Eight
Ions, Compounds, and Interpreting Formulas

Scope:

In this lecture we extend our discussion of the elements to include ions, chemical formulas, protons, electrons, and atomic weights. We will discover how electrically charged particles can cause atoms to combine and create ionic solids and molecules. We will end by exploring the units and formulas necessary to describe these structures.

Outline

I.   An atom or group of atoms can lose or gain electrons to form charged particles called ions.

    A. Atoms that gain electrons become negatively charged and are called anions.

    B. Atoms that lose electrons become positively charged and are called cations.

    C. The charge of an ion is written to the upper right of the chemical symbol, like S^{2-} or Al^{3+}.

    D. Polyatomic ions are ions that contain more than 1 atom, like OH^- or SO_4^{2-}.

II. Cations and anions attract one another and combine to form ionic solids.

    A. The proper number of positive and negative ions must combine to form an electrically neutral ionic solid.

    B. The required number of each ion is represented by a subscript in the chemical formula, like $CaCl_2$.

    C. Some chemical formulas contain parentheses to indicate the required number of ions, like $Ca(OH)_2$.

III. Molecules are made by combining 2 or more atoms and are represented by formulas.

    A. There are 7 elements that actually exist as diatomic molecules in their natural state. These are represented by formulas, not just symbols: H_2, O_2, N_2, Cl_2, Br_2, I_2, and F_2. The word "HONClBrIF" is a mnemonic device made from the symbols of the 7 elements.

    B. Some elements exist in nature as molecules with more than 2 atoms, including P_4 and S_8.

    C. When we think of molecules, we most commonly think of compounds such as H_2O or CO_2.

    D. The names of simple molecules contain prefixes to indicate the number of each in the compound. These prefixes are not used to name ionic solids.

IV. Ionic solids consist of an enormous number of ions, not individual molecules, and are represented by formula units.

V.   The atomic weight indicates how heavy the average atom of one element is compared to atoms of other elements.

    A. In addition to the protons in the nucleus, most atoms also have neutrons. Neutrons are electrically neutral (i.e., have a charge of 0).

    B. Protons and neutrons have similar masses, but electrons are much smaller.

    C. The masses of protons, neutrons, and electrons are extremely small, so the kilogram is not a convenient measurement.

    D. The atomic mass unit (amu) is used to express the mass of individual particles or atoms. One atomic mass unit equals $\frac{1}{2}$ the weight of the carbon-12 atom.

Lecture Eight—Questions
Ions, Compounds, and Interpreting Formulas

Standard Problems

1. When an atom gains 1 or more electrons, what does it form?

    A. An ion

    B. An anion

    C. A negatively charged ion

    D. All of the above

2. When an atom loses 1 or more electrons, what does it form?

    A. A cation

    B. A positively charged ion

    C. An isotope

    D. All of the above

    E. None of the above

    F. Two of the above

3. Why are positively charged ions not formed by atoms gaining protons?

4. What are the formulas and charges of each of the following polyatomic ions?

    A. Hydroxide

    B. Nitrate

    C. Sulfate

    D. Carbonate

    E. Acetate

    F. Chromate

    G. Dichromate

5. For each of the following ions, list how many of each kind of atom it contains and how many electrons the entire ion has either lost or gained.

    A. SO_3^{2-}

    B. PO_4^{3-}

    C. NH_4^+

    D. $H_3PO_4^-$

    E. $S_2O_3^{2-}$

    F. $Fe(CN)_6^{4-}$

6. Write the correct chemical formula for an ionic solid made by combining each of the following pairs of ions.

   A. Fe^{3+} and N^{3-} FeN

   B. Cr^{3+} and S^{2-} Cr_2S_3

   C. Ba^{2+} and CN^- $Ba(CN)_2$

   D. K^+ and NO_3^- KNO_3

   E. Al^{3+} and $Cr_2O_7^{2-}$ $Al(Cr_2O_7)_3$

   F. Sn^{4+} and SO_4^{2-} $Sn_2(SO_4)_4$

   G. Sn^{4+} and PO_4^{3-} $Sn_3(PO_4)_4$

7. State how many of each kind of atom are contained in each of the following compounds.

   A. $Al(C_2H_3O_2)_3$ C → 6   H → 9   O → 6

   B. $Cr_2(S_2O_3)_3$ Cr → 2   S → 6   O → 4

   C. $Fe(H_2PO_4)_3$ Fe → 1   H → 2   PO → 12

   D. $(NH_4)_2Cr_2O_7$ NH → 8   C → 2   O → 7

8. For each of the correct formulas in question 6, state how many of each kind of atom are contained in the formula.

9. Why do we say that the formula CO refers to a molecule but the formula NaCl refers to what is called a formula unit?

10. What does the atomic weight of an element tell us about the atoms of that element compared to the atoms of some other element?

11. How heavy is an aluminum atom compared to an atom of iron?

12. How heavy is an atom of Ba (element 56) compared to an atom of Ag (element 47)?

13. List the 3 fundamental particles in atoms along with their charges and their approximate masses in atomic mass units.

Advanced Problems

14. State how many atoms of each kind are contained in the following compounds.

    A. $CuSO_4 \cdot 5H_2O$

    B. $Fe_4[Fe(CN)_6]_3$

Lecture Nine
Isotopes and Families of Elements

Scope:

In this lecture we conclude our preliminary overview of the basic ideas of chemistry with a discussion of isotopes, neutrons, and mass numbers. We will also establish a more thorough grasp of the structure and organization of the periodic table of elements.

Outline

I. Isotopes are atoms of a given element that differ in the number of neutrons in their nuclei.

II. The mass number of an atom represents the total number of protons and neutrons in the nucleus, or the mass of the isotope rounded off to the nearest whole number.

    A. The actual mass of an atom is less than the calculated mass. This occurs because protons and neutrons release energy and lose mass when they combine to form a nucleus.

    B. Mass numbers are written as superscripts to the left of an element's symbol, like ^{35}Cl.

III. The number of protons, neutrons, and electrons in an isotope can be determined from the atomic number, the mass number, and the charge of an atom.

IV. The atomic weight of an element is an average weight of all isotopes of that element. Atomic weights take into consideration the weights of the different isotopes and the relative abundance of each isotope in nature.

V. The periodic table is broadly divided into different regions.

    A. The vertical columns are called groups, or families.

    B. The horizontal rows are called rows, or periods.

    C. The zigzag staircase line near the right-hand side of the table divides the elements into metals on the left and nonmetals on the right.

    D. Metals share some properties, as do nonmetals. Metals and nonmetals tend to have different properties.

    E. Metalloids are found along the zigzag staircase and have properties of both metals and nonmetals.

    F. There are 4 main sections to the periodic table: the transition elements, the inner transition elements, and 2 groups of elements called the representative or main group elements.

    G. Within these, some smaller sets of elements are classified into families.

VI. Molecular and formula weights can be calculated from individual atomic weights.

Lecture Nine—Questions
Isotopes and Families of Elements

Standard Problems

1. How many protons, neutrons, and electrons are there in each of the following?

   A. $^{59}_{27}Co$

   B. $^{197}_{79}Au$

   C. $^{52}_{24}Cr^{2+}$

   D. $^{15}_{7}N^{3-}$

   E. $^{237}_{93}Np^{3+}$

2. Distinguish between each of the following terms: atomic number, mass number, atomic weight.

3. An element X consists of 3 isotopes, ^{42}X, ^{43}X, and ^{45}X, with percent abundances of 5%, 8%, and 87%, respectively. What is a reasonable estimate of its atomic weight?

   A. 43.0

   B. 43.3

   C. 44.7

   D. Impossible to choose based on the information given.

4. What are the 2 major categories of elements in the periodic table? Which group is more abundant? What separates them on the periodic table?

5. True or false? Explain your answer.

   A. If we know an element is a metal, we can state its properties with a high degree of specificity.

   B. If we know an element is a metal, we can be certain of its general properties.

   C. If we know an element is a metal, we can make educated guesses about its general properties.

   D. Knowing an element is a metal is actually of no use when trying to guess what its properties might be.

6. A solid element is a poor conductor of heat and electricity. It shatters when struck with a hammer. Which of the following elements might it be?

   A. I_2

   B. Fe

   C. He

   D. Na

7. An unknown element forms ions with a charge of −2. Which of the following statements can you make about this element? (More than one answer may be selected).

   A. It is probably a metal.

   B. It is probably a nonmetal.

   C. It is a very reactive element.

   D. It is definitely oxygen.

8. Which of the following elements might be classified as a metalloid? More than one answer may be correct.

   A. Mg

   B. S

   C. Ne

   D. Ge

   E. Si

9. Which columns on the periodic table are referred to as the representative elements or main group elements?

10. Classify each of the following elements as an alkali metal, an alkaline earth metal, a noble gas, a halogen, or a chalcogen.

    A. Cl

    B. Ca

    C. He

    D. K

    E. S

11. Which family of elements has each of the following general properties?

    A. They form a lot of molecular compounds. When forming ionic compounds, they tend to form −2 ions.

    B. They are very reactive nonmetals. They form a lot of molecular compounds, but when forming ionic compounds they tend to form −1 ions.

    C. They are very reactive metals that tend to form +1 ions.

    D. They are metallic elements that tend to form +2 ions.

    E. They are very nonreactive elements.

12. Calculate the molecular or formula weight of each of the following compounds.

    A. $HC_2H_3O_2$

    B. $Ba(NO_3)_2$

    C. $Ca_3(PO_4)_2$

    D. $(NH_4)_3AsO_4$

Advanced Problems

13. A chemical reaction releases 350 kJ of energy. A joule (symbol J) is the unit of energy in the SI system of measurement. How much mass, in grams, was lost when this chemical reaction occurred? Hint: Use Einstein's equation $E = mc^2$. Use consistent SI units. If you substitute energy in joules and the velocity of light as 3.00×10^8 m/s, your answer will come out in kilograms.

14. Oxygen consists of 3 isotopes, ^{16}O, ^{17}O, and ^{18}O. The atomic weight of oxygen is 15.9994. How can this possibly be, if the lightest isotope has a mass number of 16 and the other 2 isotopes have mass numbers of 17 and 18?

15. Show how the average atomic weight in question 3 can be calculated. Assume that the mass numbers represent the actual masses of each isotope.

Lecture Ten
The Mole

Scope:

This lecture addresses the key topic permeating most high school chemistry problems: the mole. We explore the invention of the mole as a conceptual means of counting atoms and molecules while avoiding the physical impracticalities. We explore the mole's relationship to Avogadro's number and conclude with its quantitative definition.

Outline

I. One of the most important concepts to master in an introductory chemistry course is the mole.

II. Chemists invented the concept of the mole because they needed a way to count atoms and molecules.

    A. We need to be able to count out atoms and molecules to run chemical reactions without having anything left over.

    B. The important thing is not to literally count the actual number of atoms or molecules but to be able to obtain samples of substances that contain the same number of atoms or molecules as samples of other substances.

    C. Since atoms and molecules are far too small and far too numerous to actually count, we must be able to achieve this counting by some indirect method.

    D. Since the atomic weights of the elements tell us how heavy one atom is compared to another atom, we can weigh out equal numbers of atoms (or molecules) by simply using the ratio between the substances' atomic or molecular weights.

III. A mole of something is an amount of that substance whose weight in grams is numerically equal to its molecular weight in amus.

    A. A mole of any substance contains the same number of particles as a mole of any other substance.

    B. When the molecular weight of a substance is expressed in grams, it is referred to as the molar mass of the substance.

    C. Since we know how to calculate molecular weights, we do the same calculation but call the number obtained the molar mass, and we express it in grams per mole instead of amus per molecule.

    D. The number of particles in a mole is equal to 6.02×10^{23}, called Avogadro's number.

    E. Moles of different substances have different weights because some molecules are heavier than others.

IV. A mole is a quantity that is very analogous to a dozen.

    A. A dozen of something is 12.

    B. A mole of something is 6.02×10^{23}.

    C. What a dozen or a mole weighs depends on what it is.

Lecture Ten—Questions
The Mole

Standard Problems

1. A blue marble has a mass of 5.21 g. A yellow marble has a mass of 9.71 g. How many times heavier is a yellow marble than a blue marble? Would this relationship change if you compared the mass of 1 million yellow marbles to the mass of 1 million blue marbles?

2. When we say that water (H_2O) has a molar mass of 18.0 g/mol, what do this number and its unit tell us?

3. **A.** How many cars are there in a dozen cars?

   B. What is the weight of a dozen cars?

   C. How many tires are there on a dozen cars?

   D. How many cars are there in a mole of cars?

   E. How many tires are there in a mole of cars?

4. **A.** How many molecules are there in a mole of H_2O?

   B. How many oxygen atoms are there in a mole of H_2O?

   C. How many hydrogen atoms are there in a mole of H_2O?

5. A father and son go fishing. The father catches 9.24 kg of big fish. The son catches 2.90 kg of little fish. If a big fish weighs 0.770 kg, while a little fish weighs 0.242 kg, who caught the most fish?

6. What does a problem like the one above have to do with the mole concept?

7. Calculate the molar masses of each of the following substances.

   A. C_2H_5OH

   B. $(CH_3)_2CHNH_2$

   C. $Cu_3(AsO_4)_2$

   D. $Fe(OH)_3$

   E. $Al_2(C_2O_4)_3$

8. Avogadro's number is about 6.02×10^{23}. What are the correct units for this number?

   A. grams per molecule

   B. grams per mole

   C. molecules per gram

   D. moles per gram

   E. moles per molecule

   F. molecules per mole

9. Of the remaining 5 choices in question 8, which do you think you will be calculating and working with the most for the remainder of the course? Explain.

Advanced Problems

10. Some ionic solids, when they precipitate out of solution, form crystals that include a definite number of water molecules for every formula unit of the solid. These compounds are called hydrates. When the formulas for these compounds are written, the water molecules are included in the formula, with a dot between the formula for the ionic solid and the water molecules. The classic example is copper sulfate pentahydrate, $CuSO_4 \cdot 5H_2O$. Calculate the molar mass of copper sulfate pentahydrate.

11. Some formulas are so complicated that they require the use of parentheses within parentheses. Square brackets are typically used in place of one of the sets of parentheses. How many atoms of each element would be represented by a formula like $Fe_4[Fe(CN)_6]_3$?

Lecture Eleven
Solving Mole Problems

Scope:

By solving some problems involving moles, we will refine the quantitative techniques that we learned in earlier lectures while increasing our familiarity with this important chemical value. Specific procedures are presented that will aid in solving this type of problem, and we will conclude by practicing these procedures in different types of mole problems.

Outline

I. In this lecture several mole problems are solved.

    A. It is probably advisable to review Lectures Two and Three, which covered the basic features of quantitative reasoning as well as the general approach that should be taken when solving any type of chemistry problem.

    B. There are actually 2 goals to achieve during this lecture.

        1. We should become proficient at solving mole problems because the mole is an important recurring concept.

        2. We should sharpen our quantitative reasoning skills by developing a good understanding of the quantities used in the calculations.

    C. The quantities, or amounts, typically encountered in mole problems are grams, moles, and molecules.

    D. The this per thats encountered are grams per mole (the molar mass) and molecules per mole.

    E. Two key ideas should be kept in mind as these problems are solved.

        1. All moles contain the same number of particles, namely 6.02×10^{23}.

        2. Moles of different substances will have different masses because some molecules are heavier than others.

II. There are definite procedures that should be followed when solving the problems presented in this lecture.

III. Several different kinds of mole problems are presented and solved.

Lecture Eleven—Questions
Solving Mole Problems

Standard Problems

1. Without doing any calculations, state whether each of the following quantities represents more or less than 1 mole.
   A. 44.2 g sulfuric acid (H_2SO_4), which weighs 98.1 g/mol
   B. 85.2 g glucose ($C_6H_{12}O_6$), which weighs 180.0 g/mol
   C. 7.50×10^{22} molecules of water (H_2O), which weighs 18.0 g/mol
   D. 30.2 g nitrogen gas (N_2), which weighs 28.0 g/mol
   E. 5.19×10^{24} molecules of methane (CH_4), which weighs 16.0 g/mol
   F. 50 molecules of carbon monoxide (CO), which weighs 28.0 g/mol

2. For your birthday, a friend gives you 73.5 g glucose ($C_6H_{12}O_6$). Glucose weighs 180.0 g/mol.
   A. Did your friend give you more or less than 1 mol glucose?
   B. How many moles of glucose did your friend give you?

3. While walking in the rain, you are struck by 8.22×10^{22} molecules of water.
   A. Did you get struck by more or less than 1 mol water?
   B. How many moles of water were you struck by?

4. How many moles of methanol (CH_3OH) are contained in 82.5 g methanol?

5. What does 2.31 mol Cu weigh?

6. How many moles are there in 2.94×10^{25} molecules of CO_2?

7. If you had 23.2 mol water, how many molecules would you have?

8. What is the mass of 0.125 mol NaOH?

9. How many molecules are there in 5.21 g CO_2?

10. If you had 3.92×10^{21} molecules of HNO_3, how many grams of HNO_3 would you have?

11. Liquid bromine (Br_2) has a density of 2.91 g/mL. How many molecules of bromine are contained in a 8.50-mL sample of bromine?

Advanced Problems

12. While walking down the street, you stumble on a sphere of solid gold. The diameter of the sphere is 1.25 in. The density of gold is about 19.3 g/cm^3. If gold sells for $850.00/oz, how much is the sphere worth? The equation for the volume of a sphere is $\frac{4}{3}\pi r^3$, and there are 28.35 g to an ounce.

13. Suppose you have a small piece of gold with a mass of only 1.00 g. If you take all the atoms in that little bit of gold and lay them end to end, how far do you think they would stretch? Do not do any calculations. Just use your intuition to select what you think is the closest answer.
   A. An infinitesimal fraction of an inch—too small to see.
   B. A reasonable length—perhaps a fraction of an inch to a few feet.
   C. An enormous distance—like from Earth to the Sun or further.

14. Now let's do the calculation. If you take all the atoms in that sphere of gold with a mass of 1.00 g and lay them end to end, how far would they stretch in miles? Assume that a gold atom has an atomic radius of about 144 pm.

Lecture Twelve
Avogadro's Hypothesis and Molar Volume

Scope:

This lecture introduces the concept of molar volume, the amount of space occupied by a mole. For solids and liquids, the molar volume is different for each substance. However, for gases we will learn to use a key principle known as Avogadro's hypothesis, which states that equal volumes of different gases contain the same number of molecules, assuming the same conditions of temperature and pressure.

Outline

I.   In this lecture we consider the amount of space, or volume, occupied by a mole of any gaseous substance.

    A. The volume occupied by a mole of a substance is referred to as its molar volume.

    B. The molar volume of a solid or liquid is different for every different substance.

    C. Avogadro's hypothesis states that at the same conditions of temperature and pressure, equal volumes of different gases contain the same number of molecules.

        1. This is true because under normal conditions, gases are 99.9% empty space, so the size of the molecules themselves has very little effect on the volume occupied by a mole of molecules.

        2. Actually, equal volumes of different gases do not contain exactly the same number of molecules, but it is so close that Avogadro's hypothesis can be accepted as a very reasonable approximation.

        3. If equal volumes contain the same number of molecules, it follows that equal numbers of molecules occupy equal volumes.

    D. A mole of any gas at what chemists call standard temperature and pressure (STP) occupies a volume of 22.414 L.

        1. This holds only for gaseous substances.

        2. This is only true at STP.

II. In solving molar volume problems, the following ideas should be kept in mind.

    A. The important quantities are moles, grams, molecules, and liters.

    B. The most common this per thats are grams per mole, molecules per mole, and liters per mole.

III. Solving several practice problems will allow us to deepen our understanding of several important fundamental quantities and relationships and will also allow us to improve our general ability to reason quantitatively.

Lecture Twelve—Questions
Avogadro's Hypothesis and Molar Volume

Standard Problems

1. What is meant by the molar volume of a substance?

2. Which of the following could be units (not necessarily SI) for molar volume?

   A. Molecules per mole

   B. Grams per molecule

   C. Grams per mole

   D. Molecules per liter

   E. Liters per molecule

   F. Moles per molecule

   G. Liters per mole

   H. Cubic centimeters per molecule

   I. Microliters per mole

   J. Cubic centimeters per mole

   K. Cubic inches per mole

   L. Miles per mole

3. Why might you expect the molar volumes of different substances to be different?

4. What is an exception to the above generalization? What is it about gaseous substances that allows this to be true?

5. State Avogadro's hypothesis. Is this hypothesis exactly true?

6. One mole of any gas at STP occupies 22.414 L of space. Which of the following statements is/are true? (More than 1 may be true.)

   A. 22.414 L is larger than a large bottle of soda.

   B. 22.414 L is smaller than the average person.

   C. 22.414 L is larger than a football.

   D. 22.414 L is larger than a basketball.

7. When using the magic number 22.414 L/mol in a calculation, what conditions must be met before this number can be used?

8. State units that are typically used to express each of the following quantities.

   A. Molar mass

   B. Molar volume

   C. Avogadro's number

9. How many moles of nitrogen gas (N_2) are contained in 7.78 L at STP?

10. How many liters do 6.85 mol CO gas occupy at STP?

11. What volume is occupied by 11.27 g CO_2 gas at STP?

12. How many molecules are contained in 84.5 L CO_2 gas at STP?

13. How many grams of SF_6 are contained in 31.2 L SF_6 gas at STP?

14. What volume, in liters, is occupied by 8.15×10^{21} molecules of butane (C_4H_{10})?

15. What is the mass of 6.22 mol CO_2 gas at STP?

16. How many molecules are there in 9.92 g CO_2 gas at STP?

Advanced Problems

17. Common table salt, sodium chloride (NaCl), has a density of 2.16 g/cm³. What is the molar volume of table salt? Is your answer larger or smaller than the molar volume of a gaseous substance at STP?

18. How many liters are there in a cubic meter?

19. Neon atoms have an atomic radius of about 71 pm. What percentage of a molar volume of neon at STP is empty space?

Lecture Thirteen
Percent Composition and Empirical Formulas

Scope:

In this lecture, we encounter 2 classic types of chemistry problems: those involving percent composition and those involving empirical formulas. In the first type, we learn how to present the amounts of individual elements in a compound as percentages of total mass. In the second type, we determine the simplest formula to describe the ratios between atoms of each element in a compound. We will solve several percent composition problems in this lecture, saving our practice of empirical formula problems for later.

Outline

I. One of the classic types of problems that students learn how to solve in an introductory chemistry course is determining what is referred to as the percent composition of a compound.

  A. The term "percent composition" is always understood to mean percent composition by mass, even though it may not be specifically stated as such.

  B. Calculating the percent composition of a compound involves determining what percentage of the total mass of the compound comprises each of the elements present in the compound.

  C. There are a number of different ways in which percent composition problems can be presented.
     1. Sometimes the masses of the elements that react with each other to form a sample of the compound are given, and the percent composition is determined from this information.
     2. Sometimes the formula of the compound is given, and the percent composition can be determined from the formula.
     3. Several examples of each type of problem are presented and solved.

II. Another classic type of problem is determining what is referred to as the empirical formula of a compound.

  A. The term "empirical formula" is sometimes called the simplest formula.

  B. The empirical formula is defined as the formula of the compound written with the lowest possible whole-number ratio of the atoms of the elements in the compound.

  C. Sometimes the molecular formula and the empirical formula of a compound are different.

  D. Sometimes the molecular formula and the empirical formula of a compound are the same.

  E. The general concept of empirical formulas and how they are related to molecular formulas is presented.

  F. There are 2 reasons why chemists even bother to talk about the empirical formulas of substances rather than their actual formulas.
     1. For ionic solids, no actual molecular formula exists, since the substance comprises an enormous aggregate of ions.
     2. The only type of formula that can be discussed for the substance is an empirical formula.

Lecture Thirteen—Questions
Percent Composition and Empirical Formulas

Standard Problems

1. A sample of a compound is analyzed and found to contain 17.204 g K, 7.062 g S, and 14.080 g O. What is the percent composition of this compound?

2. A compound is formed by 1.55 g C reacting with oxygen to form a compound with a total mass of 5.68 g. What is the percent composition of this compound?

3. What is the percent composition of $(NH_4)_2CO_3$?

4. What is the percent composition of $Fe_2(MnO_4)_3$?

5. What are the empirical formulas for each of the following compounds?

    A. C_6H_6

    B. $Na_2Cr_2O_7$

    C. $C_6H_{15}N$

    D. $C_8H_{10}N_2O_2$

6. Determine the percent composition of the compound listed in question 5D.

7. Determine the percent composition of the empirical formula for the compound listed in question 5D.

Advanced Problem

8. One day, you find a wonderful money-making opportunity on the internet. Someone is willing to sell you a mineral called axinite for $9.00/kg. He furnishes you with directions on how to extract aluminum from this mineral and also directs you to another company that is willing to pay you $50.00/kg for the aluminum you can provide. Assuming the procedure actually works as advertised, is this a good opportunity to get rich? You can assume that the formula for axinite is $HCa_3Al_2BSi_4O_{16}$. Oh, and you must act *now*, because only a limited amount of axinite is available.

Lecture Fourteen
Solving Empirical Formula Problems

Scope:

We will now learn to solve the empirical formula problems that were discussed in the previous lecture. In solving these problems, it is often useful to assume a sample mass of 100 g and to express the formula in the simplest whole-number ratio of atoms. Determining the empirical formula allows us then to determine the molecular formula.

Outline

I. When determining the empirical formula of a substance from its percent composition, it is convenient to assume a sample of the substance with a mass of 100 g.

    A. Since the size of the sample of the substance does not affect its formula, any sample size could be chosen.

    B. Assuming a sample size of 100 g simplifies the mathematics involved.

II. When you calculate an empirical formula, the formula you come up with sometimes appears to contain fractions of atoms.

    A. These fractions are often halves or thirds.

    B. When this happens, it is necessary to multiply each of the subscripts in the formula by an appropriate integer to rid the formula of fractions and to obtain the simplest whole-number ratio of the atoms of the elements in the compound.

III. Molecular formulas can be determined from empirical formulas.

    A. Analyzing percent composition data only allows us to determine the simplest ratio of the atoms of the elements in the compound, not the actual molecular formula. This is the second reason why chemists bother to discuss empirical formulas.

    B. Once the empirical formula has been determined, the molecular formula can be determined by using the molar mass of the substance.

        1. The molar mass is obtained by performing an additional experiment that is capable of providing this information.

        2. The molar mass will be some integer multiple of the empirical mass, and the molecular formula will be equal to the empirical formula multiplied by this integer multiple.

IV. Several practice problems are done to illustrate how empirical and molecular formulas are determined.

Lecture Fourteen—Questions
Solving Empirical Formula Problems

Standard Problems

1. What do the subscripts in a chemical formula tell us? (More than 1 answer may be correct.)

    A. How many atoms of each element are contained in 1 molecule the substance.

    B. How many moles of each element are contained in 1 mole of the substance.

    C. How many grams of each element are contained in 1 molecule of the substance.

    D. How many grams of each element are contained in 1 mole of the substance.

2. Without doing any calculations, select all the substances listed below that would have the same percent composition.

    A. $C_4H_6O_2$

    B. C_4H_6O

    C. C_2H_3O

    D. $C_{12}H_{18}O_6$

    E. $C_8H_{12}O_4$

3. A compound containing only sulfur and oxygen is 40.07% sulfur by mass. What is the empirical formula of this compound?

4. A compound is analyzed and found to contain 13.53% Fe, 39.94% Mn, and 46.53% O. What is the empirical formula for the compound?

5. A compound containing only carbon, hydrogen, and sulfur is analyzed and found to contain 57.10% C and 4.76% H. What is the empirical formula for the compound?

6. An oxide of uranium is 84.7% U. What is its empirical formula?

7. An oxide of nitrogen has a formula N_xO_y. It is 30.43% N. If the molar mass of the compound is 92.0 g/mol, what is its molecular formula?

8. A compound has the following percent composition: 30.19% C, 5.03% H, 44.60% Cl, and 20.17% S. Its molar mass is about 159 g/mol. Determine its molecular formula.

Lecture Fifteen
Writing and Balancing Chemical Equations

Scope:

This lecture answers some fundamental questions involving chemical reactions and the equations that represent them. We will learn to identify when a chemical reaction has occurred and then to describe that reaction in a chemical equation. Once we know how to write a chemical equation, we can then balance it to conserve the atoms in the equation.

Outline

I.   In this lecture some very fundamental questions are considered.

    A. What is a chemical reaction?

    B. When we mix substances, how can we tell if a chemical reaction has occurred?

    C. How do we write equations for chemical reactions?

    D. How do we balance chemical equations, and what are we really doing when we do this?

II. What is a chemical reaction?

    A. It is a process where 1 or more substances are transformed into 1 or more different substances.

    B. What are some indications that a chemical reaction has occurred?
        1. The formation of a precipitate.
        2. The production of a gas.
        3. A color change.
        4. A temperature change that occurs even though we did not heat or cool the system ourselves.

III. A chemical reaction involves the rearrangement of the atoms present in the reactants to produce the arrangement that is present in the products.

IV. How do we write and balance chemical equations?

    A. It is very inefficient and awkward to attempt to represent chemical reactions with words.

    B. A chemical equation, in contrast, is a very efficient method for communicating what has occurred in a chemical reaction.

    C. To correctly write a chemical equation, you must know the correct formulas for all the reactants and products.

    D. The reactants are written to the left of the arrow, and the products are written to the right of the arrow.

    E. The states of the reactants and products can also be indicated in the equation.

V.   How are chemical equations balanced, and what does "balancing" really mean?

    A. When we balance a chemical equation, we are simply making sure that atoms are conserved in our equation, which is necessary because they are conserved in the actual reaction.

    B. To balance the equation, we simply search for a set of coefficients that results in both sides of the equation containing the same number of atoms of each element.

    C. Never begin by balancing atoms that appear in more than 1 substance on 1 side of the equation.

D. If the equation contains a free element—a reactant that contains only 1 kind of atom, like O_2—balance that element last.

E. If the equation contains polyatomic ions that remain the same on both sides of the equation, these ions can be balanced as entire units.

Lecture Fifteen—Questions
Writing and Balancing Chemical Equations

Standard Problems

1. Define a chemical reaction.

2. What are some indications that a chemical reaction has occurred? If you make 1 or more of these observations when you mix substances together, can you definitely conclude that a chemical reaction has occurred?

3. Which of these statements is/are true about chemical reactions? More than 1 answer may be correct.

   A. There is always an easily observable change that indicates a chemical reaction has occurred.

   B. There usually is some visual change that suggests a chemical reaction has occurred.

   C. The properties of the products are usually (but not always) related to the properties of the reactants from which they were made.

   D. New atoms are created that give the products their new properties.

   E. Chemical reactions typically involve the rearrangement of atoms.

4. If you wanted to write a correct, balanced chemical equation for a reaction that you observed in the laboratory, which of the following things would you have to determine? More than 1 answer may be correct.

   A. The correct formulas for both the reactants and products.

   B. The correct ratios of the number of molecules (or atoms or formula units) of the reactants and products involved in the reaction.

   C. The molar masses of all the reactants and products.

   D. The molar volumes of all reactants and products.

   E. How the atoms in the reactants and products were actually arranged in the different molecules.

5. When trying to balance a chemical equation, which of the following options are not allowed?

   A. Put coefficients in front of the reactants and products.

   B. Change the formulas for the reactants and products.

   C. Add whatever atoms are needed to balance the equation to either the reactant or product side of the equation.

6. Balance each of these chemical equations.

   A. $Mg + P_4 \rightarrow Mg_3P_2$

   B. $C_4H_9OH + O_2 \rightarrow CO_2 + H_2O$

   C. $N_2H_4 + O_2 \rightarrow NO_2 + H_2O$

   D. $K + H_2O \rightarrow KOH + H_2$

   E. $Br_2 + H_2O + SO_2 \rightarrow HBr + H_2SO_4$

   F. $S_8 + O_2 \rightarrow SO_3$

   G. $Na_2O_2 + H_2O \rightarrow NaOH + O_2$

H. $Ca(NO_3)_2 + FePO_4 \rightarrow Ca_3(PO_4)_2 + Fe(NO_3)_3$

I. $Mg_3N_2 + H_2O \rightarrow Mg(OH)_2 + NH_3$

J. $SO_2Cl_2 + HBr \rightarrow H_2S + HCl + Br_2 + H_2O$

7. Write and then balance the chemical equations for each of the following reactions.

A. Paraffin ($C_{25}H_{52}$) burns in oxygen to form carbon dioxide and water.

B. Silver nitrate (a compound made from Ag^+ and NO_3^-) reacts with chromium(III) chloride (a compound made from Cr^{3+} and Cl^-) to form silver chloride (a compound made from Ag^+ and Cl^-) and chromium(III) nitrate (a compound made from Cr^{3+} and NO_3^-).

Advanced Problems

8. Balance each of the following equations.

A. $S_2Cl_2 + NH_3 \rightarrow N_4S_4 + NH_4Cl + S_8$

B. $FeCr_2O_4 + Na_2CO_3 + O_2 \rightarrow Na_2CrO_4 + Fe_2O_3 + CO_2$

C. And just in case you are getting overconfident:

$XeF_4 + H_2O \rightarrow XeO_3 + Xe + HF + O_2$

9. Please realize that while in theory all chemical equations can be balanced by inspection, in practice many are essentially impossible to balance this way. Here is a rather outrageous example.

$K_4Fe(CN)_6 + KMnO_4 + H_2SO_4 \rightarrow KHSO_4 + Fe_2(SO_4)_3 + MnSO_4 + HNO_3 + CO_2 + H_2O$

The answer is in the back of this workbook, but do not waste your time trying to find it.

Lecture Sixteen
An Introduction to Stoichiometry

Scope:

We now turn to a core topic that often frustrates students of chemistry: stoichiometry, or the study of the quantitative relationships between substances in a chemical reaction. To solve stoichiometry problems, we must first look more closely at what is represented by the coefficients in a balanced chemical equation. We will examine and learn to solve the 4 basic types of stoichiometry problems.

Outline

I. Stoichiometry is the study of the quantitative relationships that exist between substances involved in a chemical reaction.

   A. The key to solving all stoichiometry problems is the balanced chemical equation for the reaction.

   B. The most important thing to understand to solve stoichiometry problems correctly is exactly what is represented by the coefficients in the balanced chemical equation.

   1. The coefficients in the balanced chemical equation can represent the ratio of molecules of the substances that are consumed or produced.

   2. The coefficients in the balanced chemical equation can represent the ratio of moles of the substances that are consumed or produced.

II. There are 4 basic types of stoichiometry problems: moles-moles, moles-grams, grams-moles, and grams-grams. However, all stoichiometry problems are really very similar, and the same general approach can be used to solve any of them.

III. Several practice problems are solved to illustrate the general approach to solving the 4 basic types of stoichiometry problems.

IV. The lecture ends with additional problems being presented and then solved.

Lecture Sixteen—Questions
An Introduction to Stoichiometry

Standard Problems

1. Select all the true statements. The coefficients in a balanced chemical equation tell you …

   A. the number of moles of reactants and products present in the container in which they are reacting.

   B. the mole ratio of the reactants and products present in the container in which they are reacting.

   C. the ratio of the masses of the reactants and products that react with each other.

   D. the mole ratios in which the reactants react with each other and the products are produced.

   E. the molecule ratio in which the reactants react with each other and the products are produced.

   F. the mole ratio in which the reactants must be reacted with each other if the reaction is going to be able to occur.

2. The next several problems will all use the following chemical equation:

   $2SO_2 + S_2Cl_2 + 3Cl_2 \rightarrow 4SOCl_2$

   A. How many moles of S_2Cl_2 are required to react with 7.00 mol SO_2?

   B. How many moles of $SOCl_2$ can be produced from 1.95 mol Cl_2?

   C. How many grams of S_2Cl_2 are needed to produce 9.21 mol $SOCl_2$?

   D. How many moles of SO_2 react with 5.00 g Cl_2?

   E. How many grams of Cl_2 react with 392.5 g S_2Cl_2?

3. The next several problems will all use the following chemical equation:

   $Ca_3P_2 + 6H_2O \rightarrow 2H_3P + 3Ca(OH)_2$

   A. How many moles of H_3P are produced along with 7.00 g $Ca(OH)_2$?

   B. How many grams of Ca_3P_2 are required to produce 6.67 mol H_3P?

   C. How many grams of $Ca(OH)_2$ can be produced from 28.39 g water?

   D. How many moles of $Ca(OH)_2$ are produced along with 4.18 mol H_3P?

4. The next several problems will all use the following chemical equation:

   $Na_2B_4O_7 + 6CaF_2 + 7SO_3 \rightarrow 4BF_3 + 6CaSO_4 + Na_2SO_4$

   A. How many moles of CaF_2 react with 0.228 mol SO_3?

   B. How many grams of $CaSO_4$ can be produced from 9.00 g $Na_2B_4O_7$?

   C. How many moles of SO_3 are needed to produce 367.3 g BF_3?

   D. How many grams of Na_2SO_4 can be produced from 6.53 mol SO_3?

Advanced Problem

5. The same internet outfit that offered you the opportunity to make money by selling you axinite from which you could extract and sell aluminum (see Lecture Thirteen's questions) has come up with another offer. They are willing to sell you an alloy of gold (Au) and copper (Cu) for an introductory price of only $25.00/g. You make money by removing the copper from the alloy using the following reaction, which we saw in the lecture:

$$3Cu + 8HNO_3 \rightarrow 3Cu(NO_3)_2 + 2NO + 4H_2O$$

After you remove the copper, you sell the gold that remains. It sounds like a good opportunity to get rich quick rather than stay in school and get a degree, but because of your past experience with this company, you decide to just order 1 oz to test the validity of the offer. You run the reaction shown and find that it takes 34.39 g HNO_3 to completely react with the copper in the 1 oz of alloy that you purchased. If gold is selling for $1,000.00/oz and there are about 28.35 g/oz, is this a good business opportunity?

Lecture Seventeen
Stoichiometry Problems

Scope:

In this lecture we will continue our discussion of stoichiometry problems. We will extend our study beyond the 4 basic types by adding units of volume, molecules, and energy. Although this may increase the complexity of the problem, the basic approach remains the same. We will also learn a few special ideas that are relevant to specific situations.

Outline

I. Even though the 4 types of stoichiometry problems appear to be different, they can all be worked by using the same basic approach.

II. In this lecture we are going to extend our study of stoichiometry to several additional types of problems.

   A. Even though this will increase the number of possible types of problems greatly, it really does not complicate things very much.

   B. All of these different problems can be solved by using the same basic type of approach.
   1. Take the substance that is given in the problem, look at the units in which it is represented, and convert this quantity into the number of moles of the substance.
   2. From the number of moles of the given substance, solve the moles-moles problem to find the number of moles of the substance requested.
   3. Take a look at what units were desired for the requested substance, then convert the moles of this substance into these units.

   C. The units that we will be adding to our mix of problems are volume of a gas at STP, molecules, and energy.
   1. The addition of these units increases the number of possible types of problems.
   2. Because the addition of these new units increases the number of possible types of problems so greatly, it is clear that no memorization approach could be successful in learning how to solve these problems.
   3. The units given should be turned into moles first. You can then work the moles-moles problem and convert your answer into whatever unit was requested.

III. The remainder of the lecture is devoted to solving several problems that illustrate the general approach that is used, as well as a few special ideas that can be applied to specific situations.

Lecture Seventeen—Questions
Stoichiometry Problems

Standard Problems

1. Describe the general approach to follow when solving almost all standard stoichiometry problems.

2. Which of these types of problems are an exception to the general rule above and can be solved without having to convert something into moles and then working a mole-mole problem? More than 1 answer may be correct.

   A. moles-moles

   B. grams-grams

   C. liter of gas at STP-molecules

   D. molecules-molecules

   E. energy-liter of gas at STP

   F. liter of gas at STP-liter of gas at STP

3. Use the following equation to solve the next set of problems:

   $$2K_2CrO_4 + 6NaCl + 16HClO_4 \rightarrow 3Cl_2(g) + 2Cr(ClO_4)_3 + 6NaClO_4 + 4KClO_4 + 8H_2O + 277 \text{ kJ}$$

   A. How many grams of $KClO_4$ can be produced from 8.35 g NaCl?

   B. How many liters of Cl_2 at STP are produced along with 29.91 g $KClO_4$?

   C. How many molecules of water are produced from 3.28 mol $HClO_4$?

   D. How many kilojoules of energy are released if 5.15 L Cl_2 gas are produced at STP?

   E. How many molecules of water must be produced to release 733 kJ energy?

   F. How many grams of $HClO_4$ react with 7.22 mol NaCl?

   G. How many molecules of Cl_2 will be produced along with 4.28×10^{25} molecules of water?

   H. How many moles of $HClO_4$ react with 3.00 mol NaCl?

4. Given this equation, answer the following questions:

   $$4C_6H_5NO_2 + 29O_2(g) \rightarrow 24CO_2(g) + 4NO_2(g) + 10H_2O$$

   A. How many liters of oxygen gas at STP are required to react with 28.5 g $C_6H_5NO_2$?

   B. How many liters of NO_2 are produced at STP if 7.33 L oxygen gas are consumed at STP?

Advanced Problems

5. Consider this general equation where A, B, C, and D represent gaseous substances, and *a, b, c, d* the coefficients in the balanced chemical equation:

   $$aA + bB \rightarrow cC + dD$$

   How many liters of D can be produced from 7.37 mol B?

6. Go back to the equation used in question 3:

$$2K_2CrO_4 + 6NaCl + 16HClO_4 \rightarrow 3Cl_2(g) + 2Cr(ClO_4)_3 + 6NaClO_4 + 4KClO_4 + 8H_2O + 277 \text{ kJ}$$

Suppose you had 15.00 g of a mixture of K_2CrO_4 and NaCl. You react this mixture with an excess of $HClO_4$ and find that when the mixture is completely reacted, 2.70 L Cl_2 are produced at STP. What percent of the mixture consisted of each of the 2 components? Look below if you want a hint.

Hint: You know that the total number of grams of the 2 components must add up to 15.00 g. Assume x grams of one component. Set up an equation for how much total Cl_2 would be produced. Some will come from one component, some from the other.

Lecture Eighteen
Advanced Stoichiometry

Scope:

Now that we have a fundamental knowledge of stoichiometry, we can move on to more advanced problems involving limiting reagents. Although these problems are more complicated, they can be solved by using a very simple approach. We will also encounter 3 terms often applied to chemical reactions: theoretical yields, actual yields, and percent yields.

Outline

I. In many chemical reactions, 1 of the reactants is completely consumed, while 1 or more of the other reactants is only partially consumed, so that some remains when the reaction is over.

  A. The substance that is completely consumed is often referred to as the limiting reagent, or limiting reactant.

  B. An analogy can be drawn between recipes used in cooking and the "recipe" for a chemical reaction. The coefficients in the balanced chemical equation essentially provide a recipe for the reaction, telling us the proper ratio in which the reactants react, so that there are no reactants remaining when the reaction is finished.

II. Limiting reagent problems can be solved by using a very simple approach.

  A. You must first determine which reactant is the limiting reagent.

  1. This can be done by comparing the actual amounts of each reactant to the amount represented in the balanced chemical equation.

  2. The reactant that allows us to run the reaction the fewest number of times is the limiting reagent.

  3. Once the limiting reagent is determined, it is used to calculate the amount of the products that can be produced.

  B. In this lecture several limiting reagent problems are presented and solved.

III. Three terms often used in chemistry are the theoretical, the actual, and the percent yield in a reaction.

  A. The theoretical yield is the amount of a substance we are capable of producing from a given amount of reactant.

  B. The actual yield is the actual amount of the substance that is produced when the reaction is run.

  C. The percent yield is the actual yield divided by the theoretical yield and multiplied by 100.

Lecture Eighteen—Questions
Advanced Stoichiometry

Standard Problems

1. What is meant by the term "limiting reactant"?

2. Given this equation, answer the following questions:

   $IF_5 + 3H_2O \rightarrow HIO_3 + 5HF$

   A. If you mixed 7.00 g IF_5 with 2.00 g H_2O, which substance would be the limiting reactant? Show calculations that support your conclusion.
   B. How many grams of HIO_3 would be produced?

3. Given this equation, answer the following questions:

   $4P_4 + 5S_8 \rightarrow 8P_2S_5$

   A. If you mixed 25.00 g P_4 with 80.00 g S_8, which substance would be the limiting reactant? Show calculations that support your conclusion.
   B. How many grams of P_2S_5 would be produced?
   C. How many grams of the excess reactant would remain when the reaction was over?

4. Given this equation, answer the following questions:

   $3Cl_2O(g) + 10H_3N \rightarrow 6NH_4Cl + 2N_2(g) + 3H_2O$

   A. If you mixed 9.22 mol Cl_2O with 500.0 g H_3N, how many grams of NH_4Cl would be produced?
   B. How many liters of N_2 gas at STP would be produced?
   C. How many grams of the excess reactant would remain when the reaction was complete?

5. Using the same equation, answer the following:

   A. If you mixed 81.3 L Cl_2O gas at STP with 155.0 g H_3N, how many grams of N_2 would be produced?
   B. What mass of the excess reactant would remain when the reaction was complete?
   C. If you actually produced 50.0 g N_2, what percent yield was achieved when the reaction was run?

Advanced Problems

6. Given this equation, answer the following questions:

   $2Sc_2O_3 + 9Cl_2(g) + 3S_2Cl_2 \rightarrow 4ScCl_3 + 6SOCl_2(g)$

   The same internet company that tried to scam you in Lectures Thirteen and Sixteen has come up with another "once-in-a-lifetime" opportunity. After apologizing for their 2 initial bad offers, they state that because you are a valuable customer whom they do not want to lose, they are ready make you an offer that is guaranteed to succeed. They will sell you 100.0 g of each of the 3 reactants needed to run the above reaction for a total cost of only $3,000.00. To prove that their offer is a sure thing, they show calculations that demonstrate that just reacting the 100.0 g Sc_2O_3 will produce over 219 g $ScCl_3$. Since $ScCl_3$ sells for $15.00/g, you are guaranteed to return of at least $3,285 on your initial $3,000 investment.

   A. Is their calculation that over 219 g $ScCl_3$ is produced if 100.0 g Sc_2O_3 is consumed correct?
   B. Is this finally a good deal? Support your conclusion with calculations.

Lecture Nineteen
An Introduction to Molarity

Scope:

This lecture examines the components of chemical solutions and introduces the important concepts of concentration and molarity. We will learn to distinguish between solutes and solvents in a solution and then to determine the concentration of a solute. Finally, we will discuss the units and relationships involved in molarity.

Outline

I. One important concept to master in any introductory chemistry course is the concept of concentration of a solution in general, as well as the specific unit of concentration referred to as the molarity of a solution.

    A. Two terms that must be distinguished from each other are solute and solvent.

        1. "Solute" refers to the substance that gets dissolved.

        2. "Solvent" refers to the substance that does the dissolving.

        3. When 2 liquids are mixed with each other, which term applies to which substance is ambiguous.

        4. For aqueous solutions, water is generally regarded as being the solvent.

        5. When a solid or gas is dissolved in a liquid, the solid or gas is generally considered to be the solute and the liquid the solvent.

    B. There are several different units of concentration used in chemistry.

        1. These different units have been developed for specific situations where they prove most useful.

        2. All units of concentration involve a ratio of either the amount of solute to solvent or the amount of solute to solution.

    C. It is important to distinguish between the amount of a solute and its concentration.

        1. "Amount" refers to the gross quantity of solute present.

        2. "Concentration" refers to the ratio of the amount of solute to solvent or solute to solution.

II. The most commonly used unit of concentration in chemistry is the unit of molarity.

    A. The symbol for molarity is M.

    B. The molarity of a solution is defined as the number of moles of solute divided by the total number of liters of solution in which this amount of solute is dissolved.

    C. A 1 M solution contains a mole of solute for every liter of solution.

        1. It is important to remember that molarity involves the total volume of the entire solution, not just the volume of solvent.

        2. The 1 M does not imply that we actually have a single mole of solute and a single liter of solution but rather is the ratio between these quantities.

        3. To prepare 1 L of a 1 M solution, you would dissolve 1 mol solute in just enough water to produce a total of 1 L solution.

Lecture Nineteen—Questions
An Introduction to Molarity

Standard Problems

1. Which of the following could be considered a valid unit with which to express the concentration of a solution? More than 1 answer may be correct.

   A. Grams of solute per milliliter of solution.

   B. Moles of solute per kilogram of solution.

   C. Liters of solute per liter of solvent.

   D. Liters of solute per cubic centimeter of solution.

   E. Moles of solute per kilogram of solvent.

   F. Molecules of solute per gram of solvent.

   G. Grams of solute per liter of solvent.

2. Suppose you had a 1.00 M solution of HCl. Which of the following statements regarding this solution is correct? More than 1 answer may be correct.

   A. You have 1 mol HCl and 1 L solution.

   B. If you had 1 L solution, it would contain 1 mol HCl.

   C. You could have only $\frac{1}{2}$ L solution and it could still be 1.00 M HCl.

   D. If you had 2 L solution, it would contain 2 mol HCl.

   E. If you had $\frac{1}{2}$ L solution, it would contain 2 mol HCl.

   F. You have the same number of moles of HCl as you have liters of solution.

   G. To make this solution, you could mix 1 mol HCl with 1 L water.

3. Describe how you might prepare 250 mL of a 1.00 M solution of NaOH. NaOH has a molar mass of 40.0 g/mol.

4. Two solutions of vegetable dye are prepared. One is made by adding 8 drops of dye to a 2.00-L volumetric flask filled with water. The other is prepared by adding 1 drop of vegetable dye to 250 mL of water. Which solution will be darker in color?

Lecture Twenty
Solving Molarity Problems

Scope:

In this lecture we extend our understanding of molarity by solving some typical molarity problems that students might encounter in a high school chemistry class. Again, our approach to these problems will be based on deep understanding of the concepts involved, not meaningless memorization of formulas. You will be asked to draw on your natural logic in solving several practice molarity problems.

Outline

I. In this lecture we are going to learn how to solve some typical high school–level molarity problems.

    A. Keep in mind as we approach these problems that our goal is not to find some formula or method by which we can obtain the correct answers to the problems without having to understand the concept of molarity.

    B. What we want to do as we work through these problems is to think deeply about the concept of molarity, try to visualize the problems as they are presented, and then use our natural ability to reason quantitatively and obtain the correct answers.

    C. It is probably not a good idea to try to solve molarity problems by just using the formula for molarity.

    D. A general approach to molarity problems might be something like the following.

        1. Take time to think about what is really being represented by the quantities given in the problem. If necessary, draw a picture or diagram of the problem.

        2. After really thinking about what the quantities represent, put the numbers together in a logical manner.

        3. Check your answer by using the molarity formula or factor-label method if necessary.

II. Several practice problems are presented and solved.

Lecture Twenty—Questions
Solving Molarity Problems

Standard Problems

1. If 0.423 mol NaCl are dissolved in water to produce 250 mL solution, what is the molarity of this solution?

2. What is the molarity of a solution prepared by dissolving 255 g Na_2WO_4 in enough water to produce 388 mL solution?

3. Describe how you would prepare 500 mL of a 1.25 M solution of K_2CrO_4.

4. How many moles of HNO_3 are contained in 125 mL of a 0.333 M solution?

5. How many grams of H_2SO_4 are contained in 38.0 mL of a 2.22 M solution?

6. How many milliliters of 0.25 M HNO_3 contain the same number of moles of HNO_3 as 250 mL of 0.75 M HNO_3?

7. An experiment calls for 3.44 mol NaOH. How many milliliters of a 6.00 M solution of NaOH are required?

8. An experiment calls for 50.00 g $C_{12}H_{22}O_{11}$. How many milliliters of a 3.00 M solution of $C_{12}H_{22}O_{11}$ are required?

Advanced Problem

9. A solution of $C_{12}H_{22}O_{11}$ has a density of 1.15 g/mL. If it required 922 mL of water to prepare 1.00 L of the solution, what is the solution's molarity? The density of pure water is 1.00 g/mL.

Lecture Twenty-One
Advanced Molarity Problems

Scope:

This lecture presents some challenging new problems that will require you to draw on many of the skills learned in previous lectures. Some of these problems may be difficult at first, but successfully solving them can be considered proof that you have mastered the concepts and procedures presented so far.

Outline

I. In this lecture we take what we learned about molarity and apply this knowledge to a few additional types of problems.

    A. This is a very challenging task because no sample problems of this type have been modeled or solved in previous lectures.

    B. Solving any of these problems correctly can be taken as an indication of mastery of both the specific concepts previously covered and the general approach to thinking about problems offered throughout this series of lectures.

    C. If you encounter difficulty in solving the problems, that is to be expected.

    D. Some of these problems have specific names, such as dilution problems.

        1. In some cases, special formulas are presented for solving the specific problems.

        2. Despite this, because there actually is nothing different about these problems, no special formulas or approaches are required.

II. The remainder of the lecture consists of several problems being presented and solved.

Lecture Twenty-One—Questions
Advanced Molarity Problems

Standard Problems (Some of these are actually somewhat advanced.)

1. What is the concentration of a solution prepared by diluting 50 mL of 6.0 M HCl with 50 mL water?

2. What volume of 3.25 M NaOH is needed to prepare 500 mL of a 1.00 M solution?

3. An experiment calls for 500 mL of a 0.50 M solution of acetic acid ($HC_2H_3O_2$). A stock bottle labeled "glacial acetic acid" is known to actually be 17.4 M acetic acid.

   A. How many milliliters of the glacial acetic acid are needed to prepare the 500 mL of 0.50 M acetic acid?

   B. Describe how you would actually go about preparing this solution.

4. If 125 mL of a 1.88 M solution of HCl are mixed with 722 mL of a 0.63 M solution of HCl, what is the concentration of the final HCl solution?

5. Consider this reaction:

   $AgNO_3(aq) + NaCl(aq) \rightarrow AgCl(s) + NaNO_3(aq)$

   How many milliliters of 1.35 M $AgNO_3$ solution are required to produce 9.00 g AgCl precipitate?

6. Consider this reaction:

   $FeS(s) + 2HI(aq) \rightarrow H_2S(g) + FeI_2(aq)$

   What volume of 5.00 M M HI is needed to produce 6.4 L H_2S gas at STP?

7. What are the concentrations of Na^+ and PO_4^{3-} ions in a 0.42 M solution of Na_3PO_4?

8. What are the concentrations of each ion in each of the following solutions?

   A. 0.18 M NaCl

   B. 1.93 M $NaNO_3$

   C. 4.82 M K_2SO_3

   D. 0.87 M $Al_2(SO_4)_3$

9. If 6.12 g $Fe_2(SO_4)_3$ is dissolved in water to produce 85 mL of solution, what are the concentrations of Fe^{3+} and SO_4^{2-} in this solution?

10. Consider this reaction:

    $3SnCl_4(aq) + 4K_3PO_4(aq) \rightarrow 12KCl(aq) + Sn_3(PO_4)_4(s)$

    Suppose 225 mL of a 1.85 M solution of $SnCl_4$ were mixed with 350 mL of a 1.77 M solution of K_3PO_4.

    A. Which substance is the limiting reactant? Show calculations that support your conclusion.

    B. How many grams of $Sn_3(PO_4)_4$ would be produced?

Advanced Problem

11. For question 10B, what are the concentrations of the 2 ions that are in excess when the reaction is complete?

Lecture Twenty-Two
Basic Concepts of Chemical Equilibrium

Scope:

We continue our study of chemical reactions by examining an important new component: the equilibrium system. We begin by looking carefully at the difference between reactions that go to completion and those that are reversible and reach a state of apparent stasis. This will bring us to our examination of equilibrium systems and how to achieve them in a chemical reaction. We conclude by learning how to graphically present a system that is approaching equilibrium.

Outline

I. Some chemical reactions are said to go to completion, while other chemical reactions are said to be reversible.

    A. When we say that a reaction goes to completion, we mean that the reactants continue to react with each other until one of them is completely consumed and we have formed as much product as possible.

    B. When we say that a reaction is reversible, we mean that the reaction does not continue until all of at least one of the reactants is consumed.

        1. In principle, all chemical reactions are reversible, although for practical purposes many can be considered to go to completion.

        2. With reversible reactions, the system achieves a state where, although the reactants have not completely converted to products, the reaction appears to have ceased.

        3. Actually, the reactions have not ceased at all. In fact, the forward and reverse reactions are still occurring but at equal and opposite rates, producing a situation where the concentrations of the substances present in the system do not change with time.

II. There are several important ideas to keep in mind when thinking about equilibrium systems.

    A. When setting up an equilibrium system, it is not necessary to mix the substances involved in the equilibrium in the mole ratio obtained from the balanced chemical equation for the reaction.

    B. The amounts of substances present when equilibrium is achieved (and even the ratio of the amounts of substances present) need not bear any relationship whatsoever to the coefficients of these substances in the balanced chemical equation for the reaction.

    C. The coefficients in the balanced chemical equation only tell you the mole ratio in which the substances react with each other.

    D. Equilibrium is achieved when the rates of the forward and reverse reactions become equal.

        1. This means that the reactants are being converted into products at the same rate that the products are being reconverted into reactants.

        2. The fact that the rates of the forward and reverse reactions are equal in no way implies that there will be equal amounts of reactants and products present at equilibrium.

        3. Although the actual rates of the forward and reverse reactions are equal at equilibrium, one reaction will have the faster intrinsic rate.

III. We can graphically represent a system approaching equilibrium by plotting the concentrations of all the substances present in the equilibrium versus time.

    A. We will consider such a graph for the general reaction $2A + B \leftrightarrow C + 3D$.

    B. Several important ideas about equilibrium systems can be illustrated by such a graph.

Lecture Twenty-Two—Questions
Basic Concepts of Chemical Equilibrium

Standard Problems

1. What do we mean when we say that a reaction goes to completion?

2. What are the characteristics of what we are calling a reversible reaction?

3. Select all of the true statements from among the following for a chemical system that has achieved a state of equilibrium.

    A. There are no longer any visibly observable changes occurring in the system.

    B. The rates of the forward and reverse reactions are equal.

    C. The number of moles of reactants and products will be equal.

    D. The number of grams of reactants and products will be equal.

    E. The mole ratios of the reactants and products can be different from their ratios in the balanced chemical equation.

4. Select all of the true statements from among the following.

    A. When a reaction begins with only reactants, the concentration of the products will continue to increase until the system has achieved a state of equilibrium.

    B. When a reaction begins with only reactants, the concentration of the reactants will continue to decrease until the system has achieved a state of equilibrium.

    C. In the reaction $2A + 3B \leftrightarrow C + 4D$, as the system approaches equilibrium, the concentration of A will change at twice the rate at which the concentration of C increases.

    D. In the reaction $2A + 3B \leftrightarrow C + 4D$, if we start with only A and B, the concentration of D at equilibrium will be 4 times the concentration of C.

    E. In the reaction $2A + 3B \leftrightarrow C + 4D$, if we start with only A and B, the concentration of B at equilibrium will be $\frac{3}{2}$ the concentration of A.

    F. In the reaction $2A + 3B \leftrightarrow C + 4D$, if we start with 10.0 mol A and only 1.0 mol B, the concentration of B will still fall at 1.5 times the rate at which the concentration of A falls.

5. What is the one thing that the coefficients in the balanced chemical equation for a reversible chemical reaction tell you?

6. Consider this hypothetical reaction:

    $3A + B \leftrightarrow 4C + 2D$

    First, 7.00 mol A and 2.00 mol B are placed in 1.00 -L container and allowed to reach equilibrium. At equilibrium, the number of moles of D are measured, and it is found that 1.50 mol D were formed at equilibrium. Calculate the number of moles of A, B, and C that would be present at equilibrium.

Lecture Twenty-Three
An Introduction to the Equilibrium Constant

Scope:

In this lecture we will hone our understanding of chemical equilibrium by tracking and graphing a hypothetical reaction as it approaches a state of equilibrium. We will then examine a concept that is key to understanding equilibrium: the equilibrium constant. While the equilibrium constant is difficult to grasp intuitively, establishing a familiarity with it will allow us to consider it more comprehensively later.

Outline

I. In this lecture we take a close look at the hypothetical reaction $2A + B \leftrightarrow C + 3D$.

    A. Beginning with several different initial concentrations of reactants and products, we watch the system as it approaches and finally attains equilibrium.

    B. These processes can be nicely represented on graphs of the concentrations of all reactants and products versus time.

        1. We find that after a period of time, all concentrations become constant, indicating that the systems have achieved equilibrium states.

        2. Looking at the equilibrium concentrations of the reactants and products after equilibrium is attained, it would appear that each state is completely independent of the other states and that they have absolutely nothing in common.

II. The single most important thing to understand about equilibrium is the form and nature of the equilibrium constant.

    A. For every equilibrium system at a given temperature, there exists a specific equilibrium constant.

        1. This constant is usually symbolized by K, K_{eq}, or K_c. (We will use simply K.)

        2. The mathematical form of the equilibrium constant for a reaction, while difficult to state in words, is easy to represent symbolically.

        3. This constant will always have the same numerical value at a given temperature, no matter what the individual concentrations of the various reactants and products.

    B. While the existence of such a constant is not easy to understand intuitively, it is fairly easy to demonstrate theoretically why such a constant should exist, although such a demonstration is beyond what we will be covering in this series of lectures.

    C. Heterogeneous reactions involve reactants or products that are pure solids or liquids.

        1. When writing the equilibrium constant expressions for these reactions, the pure solids and pure liquids are omitted from the expressions.

        2. Several examples are done to illustrate the correct method of writing expressions for heterogeneous reactions.

Lecture Twenty-Three—Questions
An Introduction to the Equilibrium Constant

Standard Problems

1. Consider the equilibrium system $2A + B \leftrightarrow 3C + D$. Then select all of the statements that are true of this system from among the following.

    A. The coefficients for this reaction tell you that at equilibrium you will have to have more C and D than A and B.

    B. If you start with only A and B, the concentration of C at equilibrium will be 3 times the concentration of D.

    C. If you start with 1.00 mol each of A, B, C, and D, the concentration of C at equilibrium will be 3 times the concentration of D.

    D. The value for the equilibrium constant for this reaction will depend on the initial starting concentrations of the reactants and products.

    E. Looking at the coefficients in the balanced equation will allow us to estimate the value of the equilibrium constant for this reaction.

2. Write the correct equilibrium constant expression (K) for each of the following reactions.

    A. $HF(aq) \leftrightarrow H^+(aq) + F^-(aq)$

    B. $2NOBr(g) \leftrightarrow 2NO(g) + Br_2(g)$

    C. $N_2O(g) + 4H_2(g) \leftrightarrow 2NH_3(g) + H_2O(g)$

    D. $2KNO_3(s) \leftrightarrow 2KNO_2(s) + O_2(g)$

    E. $2Na(s) + 2H_2O(l) \leftrightarrow 2Na^+(aq) + 2OH^-(aq) + H_2(g)$

    F. $3CH_3CH_2OH(aq) + 2Cr_2O_7^{2-}(aq) + 16H^+(aq) \leftrightarrow 3CH_3COOH(aq) + 4Cr^{3+}(aq) + 11H_2O(l)$

    G. $8H_3N(aq) + 3Cl_2(g) \leftrightarrow N_2(g) + 6NH_4Cl(aq)$

Advanced Problem

3. In Lecture Twenty-Three, several graphs were presented to show how the concentrations of each of the reactants and products changed as a system approached equilibrium. It was stated that the initial sloping lines, although drawn as straight lines on some of the graphs, should actually be slightly curved. Why is that?

Lecture Twenty-Four
Interpreting an Equilibrium Constant

Scope:

In this lecture we become more familiar with the quantitative aspects of the equilibrium constant. We find that for any reaction at a given temperature, the equilibrium constant is always satisfied, no matter the individual concentrations in the solution. By working some sample equilibrium problems, we can interpret what the equilibrium constant means for each system.

Outline

I. For every reaction at a given temperature, there exists an equilibrium constant that is always satisfied when the system is at equilibrium, no matter what the individual concentrations of the reactants and products.

    A. The nature and numerical value of the equilibrium constant is probably the single most important thing to understand about any equilibrium reaction.

    B. The range of possible numerical values for equilibrium constants ranges from almost zero to almost infinity.

        1. If the value for the equilibrium constant is large (greater than 1), chemists say that "the products are favored," or "equilibrium lies to the right."

        2. If the value for the equilibrium constant is small (less than 1), chemists say that "the reactants are favored," or "equilibrium lies to the left."

        3. If the value for the equilibrium constant is large, you tend to have more products than reactants at equilibrium, while if the value for the equilibrium constant is small, you tend to have more reactants than products at equilibrium.

    C. When presented with an equilibrium problem, you can always begin by writing down the expression for the equilibrium constant for the system and setting it equal to the numerical value for the equilibrium constant.

    D. Equilibrium constants are usually measured under standard state conditions, namely 25°C and 1 atm of pressure.

II. This lecture concludes by looking at some actual equilibrium systems and their equilibrium constants and interpreting what these constants tell us about each system.

Lecture Twenty-Four—Questions
Interpreting an Equilibrium Constant

Standard Problems

1. How many times does the letter "a" appear in the word "equilibrium"?

2. Why is such a big deal made about the importance of the equilibrium constant?

3. Why can equilibrium constants not have negative values?

4. What is the possible numerical range for equilibrium constants?

5. An equilibrium constant has a very large value: $K = 3.80 \times 10^{21}$. Consider each of the following statements regarding what this large value is supposed to indicate and state whether it is absolutely true, probably true, definitely false, probably false, or a reasonable but somewhat ambiguous interpretation, and justify your choice of answer.

    A. At equilibrium, there will be more moles of reactants than products.

    B. At equilibrium, there will be more moles of products than reactants.

    C. At equilibrium, the products are favored.

    D. Equilibrium for this reaction lies to the right.

6. Consider these 3 chemical reactions and their respective equilibrium constants.

    Reaction 1: $2SO_2(g) + O_2(g) \leftrightarrow 2SO_3(g)$, $K = 2.7$

    Reaction 2: $2H_2(g) + O_2(g) \leftrightarrow 2H_2O$, $K = 1.40 \times 10^{83}$

    Reaction 3: $N_2(g) + 2O_2(g) \leftrightarrow 2NO_2(g)$, $K = 1.70 \times 10^{-17}$

    Suppose you started each of these reactions by putting 1 mole of each of the reactants and products into a 1.00-L container.

    A. For which reaction would you still have considerable amounts of all reactants and products when the system achieves equilibrium?

    B. For which reaction would there be only a negligible amount of product be present at equilibrium?

    C. For which reaction would the concentration of one of the reactants fall to essentially zero? What would be the equilibrium concentration of the other reactant?

Advanced Problems

7. Consider this chemical reaction:

    $A + B \leftrightarrow C + D$, $K = 4.00$

    A. What would be the equilibrium constant for the reverse reaction, $C + D \leftrightarrow A + B$?

    B. What would be the equilibrium constant for the reaction $2A + 2B \leftrightarrow 2C + 2D$?

    C. What would be the equilibrium constant for the reaction $\frac{1}{2}C + \frac{1}{2}D \leftrightarrow \frac{1}{2}A + \frac{1}{2}B$?

Lecture Twenty-Five
Le Chatelier's Principle—Concentration

Scope:

This lecture introduces us to a very useful tool in chemistry known as Le Chatelier's principle. While Le Chatelier's principle does not help us describe the quantitative aspects of an equilibrium system, it does allow us to make qualitative judgments about the system—for instance, whether the equilibrium constant will change under altered conditions, and if so, in what direction. While the principle can be stated in many ways, it basically asserts that a system will attempt to shift in such a way as to counteract whatever stress is applied to it.

Outline

I. Equilibrium systems are very changeable.

    A. The only way to quantitatively determine the result of altered conditions is to actually work a numerical equilibrium problem.

    B. If you only want a qualitative idea about what happens to an equilibrium system when conditions are changed, you can often achieve this by using Le Chatelier's principle.

II. Le Chatelier's principle is an extremely useful qualitative tool in chemistry.

    A. It is really more of a game than a rigorous scientific principle.

    B. Le Chatelier's principle cannot provide quantitative answers in most cases.

    C. Le Chatelier's principle can do the following.

        1. It can tell us the direction in which a system at equilibrium will shift.

        2. It can tell us whether the amounts and concentrations of the reactants and products in the new equilibrium will be larger or smaller than the amounts and concentrations of these substances in the original equilibrium.

        3. It can tell us whether the equilibrium constant for the reaction will change, and if it does, whether it will increase or decrease.

    D. Le Chatelier's principle can be stated in various ways.

        1. We will state the principle as follows: If a stress is applied to a system at equilibrium, the system will shift, if possible, in the direction that completely or at least partially alleviates the stress.

        2. There are several important points to keep in mind when applying this principle.

            a. The system should be at equilibrium before the stress is applied.

            b. The term "stress" means a change in the concentration of one of the reactants or products, a change in pressure, or a change in temperature.

            c. "Shifting" means converting some reactants to products or products to reactants.

            d. There are some situations where the system cannot do anything about the stress.

            e. In some cases the system can completely alleviate the stress, but more often it can only partially alleviate the stress.

        3. A simple way to state Le Chatelier's principle is to say that whatever you do to a system at equilibrium, the system will try to do the opposite.

III. We will begin our application of Le Chatelier's principle by considering changes in the concentration of one of the reactants or products.

Lecture Twenty-Five—Questions
Le Chatelier's Principle—Concentration

Standard Problems

1. Assemble the following sentence fragments into a correct statement of Le Chatelier's principle.

   the system will shift

   or at least partially

   if a stress is applied

   that completely

   alleviates the stress

   to a system at equilibrium

   if possible

   in the direction

2. What is meant by the term "stress" when it is applied to a chemical system?

3. Consider this equilibrium system:

   $2C_6H_6(g) + 15O_2(g) \leftrightarrow 12CO_2(g) + 6H_2O(g)$, $\Delta H = -6340$ kJ

   If additional CO_2 were added to this system …

   A. Which way would the system shift?

   B. What would happen to the concentration of each reactant and product?

   C. What would happen to the value for K?

4. Consider this equilibrium system:

   $2Fe^{2+} + Sn^{4+} \leftrightarrow 2Fe^{3+} + Sn^{2+}$

   If the concentration of Sn^{2+} were decreased …

   A. Which way would the system shift?

   B. What would happen to the concentration of each reactant and product?

   C. What would happen to the value for K?

5. Consider this equilibrium system:

   $2NOBr(g) \leftrightarrow 2NO(g) + Br_2(g)$

   If additional NO were added to the system …

   A. Which way would the system shift?

   B. What would happen to the concentration of each reactant and product?

   C. What would happen to the value for K?

   If Br_2 were removed from this system …

   D. Which way would the system shift?

   E. What would happen to the concentration of each reactant and product?

   F. What would happen to the value for K?

6. Consider this equilibrium system:

$$H_2O(l) \leftrightarrow H^+ + OH^-$$

If the concentration of H^+ were increased …
   A. Which way would the system shift?
   B. What would happen to the concentration of each reactant and product?
   C. What would happen to the value for K?

Advanced Problem

7. Calculate the molarity of pure water. The density of water is 1.00 g/mL.

Lecture Twenty-Six
Le Chatelier—Pressure and Temperature

Scope:

Having established a basic understanding of Le Chatelier's principle, we will now explore the various ways in which this principle can manifest itself when an equilibrium system is changed. Specifically, we will examine circumstances in which the pressure or temperature of a system is changed. By applying Le Chatelier's principle, we will be able to qualitatively predict the system's reaction to these changes.

Outline

I. In this lecture we are going to see how Le Chatelier's principle can be used to predict the effect of a change in pressure or temperature on an equilibrium system.

    A. When we refer to a change in pressure, we always mean a change in pressure brought about by a change in the volume of the system.

        1. There are other ways of changing the pressure of a system, such as adding or removing a gaseous reactant or product or changing the temperature.

            a. Neither of these changes are treated as pressure changes.

            b. Adding or removing a gaseous reactant or product is treated as a change in concentration.

            c. Changing the pressure by changing the temperature is simply treated as a change in temperature.

        2. Pressure changes are only relevant to equilibrium systems that contain at least 1 gaseous reactant or product.

    B. If we increase the pressure on the system, the system will try to decrease the pressure, and vice versa.

        1. The only way it is able to alter the pressure is to either shift to the right or to the left.

        2. A system can decrease its own pressure by shifting in the direction where there are fewer gaseous molecules, and vice versa.

    C. When dealing with changes in an equilibrium system brought about changes in pressure, we must be careful to only specify what happens to the amounts of reactants and products, not their concentrations.

        1. The change in the amounts of reactants and products can be unambiguously predicted by Le Chatelier's principle.

        2. What happens to the concentrations of the reactants and products is sometimes ambiguous because the concentrations of all reactants and products were immediately changed when the initial volume of the system was altered.

    D. Changing the pressure cannot change the value of K.

    E. When counting molecules to determine which way a system will shift in response to a change in pressure, only gaseous molecules should be counted.

    F. If a system contains the same number of gaseous molecules on both sides of the equation, it cannot react to a change in pressure.

    G. To predict how an equilibrium system will respond to a change in temperature, we must know whether the reaction is exothermic or endothermic.

        1. If temperature is raised, the system will try to lower the temperature by shifting in the endothermic direction.

2. If temperature is lowered, the system will try to raise the temperature by shifting in the exothermic direction.
3. Changing temperature will change the value of K.

Lecture Twenty-Six—Questions
Le Chatelier—Pressure and Temperature

Standard Problems

1. Which of the following can we accomplish by applying Le Chatelier's principle?

   A. We can tell in which direction an equilibrium will shift in reaction to a stress.

   B. If the equilibrium constant changes in reaction to a stress, we can tell whether it will increase or decrease.

   C. We can tell how the amounts of reactants and products in an equilibrium system after it reacts to a stress will compare to the amounts present in the system before the stress was applied.

   D. For concentration stresses, we can tell qualitatively (without actual numerical values) how the concentration of the reactants and products in the system after it has reacted to a stress will compare to their concentrations before the stress was applied.

   E. For temperature stresses, we can tell qualitatively how the concentration of the reactants and products in the system after it has reacted to a stress will compare to their concentrations before the stress was applied.

   F. For pressure stresses, we can always tell qualitatively how the concentration of the reactants and products in the system after it has reacted to a stress will compare to their concentrations before the stress was applied.

   G. We can determine in which direction a reaction will move before it establishes equilibrium.

2. Consider this equilibrium system:

   $2C_6H_6(g) + 15O_2(g) \leftrightarrow 12CO_2(g) + 6H_2O(g)$, $\Delta H = -6340$ kJ

   If additional O_2 were added to this system …

   A. In which direction would the system shift?

   B. What would happen to the concentration of each reactant and product?

   C. What would happen to the value of K?

   If the pressure of this system were decreased …

   D. In which direction would the system shift?

   E. What would happen to the amount of each reactant and product?

   F. What would happen to the value of K?

   If the temperature of this system were increased …

   G. In which direction would the system shift?

   H. What would happen to the concentration of each reactant and product?

   I. What would happen to the value of K?

3. Consider this equilibrium system:

   $CO(g) + 3H_2(g) \leftrightarrow H_2O(g) + CH_4(g)$, $\Delta H = -230$ kJ

   If water vapor were removed from this system …

   A. In which direction would the system shift?

   B. What would happen to the concentration of each reactant and product?

   C. What would happen to the value of K?

If the volume of this system were decreased …

D. In which direction would the system shift?

E. What would happen to the amount of each reactant and product?

F. What would happen to the value of K?

If the temperature of this system were increased …

G. In which direction would the system shift?

H. What would happen to the concentration of each reactant and product?

I. What would happen to the value of K?

Advanced Problems

4. Consider this equilibrium system:

$N_2(g) + 3H_2(g) \leftrightarrow 2NH_3(g)$

Suppose this system is enclosed in a solid, sealed container with enough of all the reactants and products to produce a total pressure of 1.88 atm.

A. If the pressure inside this system were raised to 2.88 atm by injecting helium gas into the container, which way would the system shift?

B. If helium gas were injected into this system but the system were allowed to change its volume to keep the total pressure at 1.88 atm, which way would the system shift?

Lecture Twenty-Seven
An Introduction to Equilibrium Problems

Scope:

Now that we understand some fundamental qualities of equilibrium systems, we can try our hands at solving equilibrium problems. While it may take practice to become comfortable with these problems, the only knowledge essential to solving them is how to write and interpret equilibrium constants. With this knowledge in hand, we will learn how to approach several different types of equilibrium problems.

Outline

I. Once a good understanding of the basic nature of equilibria is achieved, it is possible to tackle the solving of equilibrium problems.

   A. In principle, the only essential thing that must be understood to work any equilibrium problem is how to write and interpret the meaning of an equilibrium constant.

   B. While the solving of equilibrium problems does not require learning very much more about equilibria in general, it usually takes a lot of exposure and practice to become fluent at the task.

II. Equilibrium problems can be conveniently separated into different types.

   A. One of the easiest types gives you the equilibrium concentrations of the reactants and products in some system and then asks you to calculate the numerical value of the equilibrium constant for the reaction.

   B. Another type gives you the numerical value for the equilibrium constant for a reaction, the equilibrium concentrations of all reactants and products except 1, and then asks you to find the equilibrium concentration of this substance.

   C. When solving equilibrium problems one must be very careful to distinguish initial concentrations from equilibrium concentrations.

   D. Although they can be divided into different types, all equilibrium problems involve applying the very same principles and are not really different in any important way.

III. Several equilibrium problems are presented and solved.

Lecture Twenty-Seven—Questions
An Introduction to Equilibrium Problems

Standard Problems

1. Consider this equilibrium system:

   $2A + 3B \leftrightarrow C + 2D$

   If at equilibrium, [A] = 1.72 M, [B] = 0.815 M, [C] = 0.0783 M, and [D] = 2.24 M, calculate the value of K for this reaction.

2. Consider this equilibrium system:

   $HF(aq) \leftrightarrow H^+(aq) + F^-(aq)$

   If at equilibrium, [HF] = 0.250 M, [H$^+$] = 1.30×10^{-2} M, and [F$^-$] = 1.30×10^{-2} M, calculate the value of the equilibrium constant for this reaction.

3. Consider this equilibrium system:

   $A + 2B \leftrightarrow 3C + D, K = 4.2 \times 10^{-3}$

   If at equilibrium, [B] = 4.38 M, [C] = 0.15 M, and [D] = 0.27 M, what will be the equilibrium concentration of A?

4. Consider this equilibrium system:

   $2A + 3B \leftrightarrow 2C + D, K = 7.3 \times 10^{-2}$

   If at equilibrium, [B] = 5.11 M, [C] = 4.22 M, and [D] = 3.19 M, what will be the equilibrium concentration of A?

5. Consider this equilibrium system:

   $PbI_2(s) \leftrightarrow Pb^{2+} + 2I^-, K = 7.1 \times 10^{-9}$

   If at equilibrium, [Pb^{2+}] = 0.064 M, what will be the concentration of I$^-$?

6. Consider this equilibrium system:

   $2H_2S(g) \leftrightarrow 2H_2(g) + S_2(g)$

   When 1.00 mole of H$_2$S is placed in a 100-L container and is allowed to establish equilibrium, the concentration of H$_2$ is measured and found to be equal to 0.38 M. From this information, calculate the value of K for this reaction.

7. Consider this reaction:

   $CO(g) + H_2O(g) \leftrightarrow CO_2(g) + H_2(g)$

   When 1.50 mol of CO and 1.50 mol H$_2$O are injected into a 1.00-L container and equilibrium is achieved, the concentration of CO$_2$ is measured and found to be 1.25 M. What is the value of the equilibrium constant for this reaction?

Advanced Problem

8. Consider this hypothetical reaction:

$$3A + 2B \leftrightarrow C + 5D$$

So 4.00 mol A and 5.00 mol B are placed in a 2.00-L container and are allowed to establish equilibrium. Given that the equilibrium concentration of C is 0.35 M, calculate the value of the equilibrium constant for this reaction.

Lecture Twenty-Eight
The Self-Ionization of Water

Scope:

In this lecture, we will explore one of the most important equilibria that exist in nature: the self-ionization of water. After examining the categories of substances that are liquid or that can be dissolved in water, we will learn the basic quantitative characteristics of the self-ionization of water and solve some problems using this information. The lecture will end with a brief introduction to the pH of solutions.

Outline

I. One of the most important equilibria that exist in nature is the equilibrium that exists in water, called the self-ionization of water.

    A. Substances that are liquids or that dissolve in water are often divided into 3 broad categories.

        1. These categories are nonelectrolytes, strong electrolytes, and weak electrolytes.

            a. Nonelectrolytes do not conduct electricity.

            b. Strong electrolytes conduct electricity very well.

            c. Weak electrolytes conduct electricity to a small extent.

        2. The key to whether a substance conducts electricity and how well it does so is whether or not it forms ions in solution.

            a. Nonelectrolytes are made of molecules and remain molecules when dissolved in water.

            b. Strong electrolytes exist in water only as ions.

            c. Weak electrolytes dissolve in water to form mostly molecules, but a small percentage of the molecules break apart to form ions.

        3. Water is classified as a weak electrolyte.

    B. The self-ionization of water can be represented by the equation $H_2O(l) \leftrightarrow H^+(aq) + OH^-(aq)$.

        1. The equilibrium constant for this reaction is called the ion product of water.

            a. It is represented by the symbol K_w.

            b. $K_w = [H^+][OH^-] = 1.00 \times 10^{-14}$ at 25°C.

        2. If the concentration of hydrogen ions in an aqueous solution is high, the concentration of hydroxide ions must be low, and vice versa.

II. Several problems related to the ion product of water are presented and solved.

III. The pH of a solution is defined as $-\log[H^+]$.

    A. The pH of an acidic solution is less than 7, the pH of a neutral solution is equal to 7, and the pH of a basic solution is greater than 7.

    B. The logarithm of a number is the power to which 10 must be raised to obtain the number.

Lecture Twenty-Eight—Questions
The Self-Ionization of Water

Standard Problems

1. What was the purpose of doing the conductivity demonstration in the lecture? What are some important things that could have been learned from that demonstration?

2. What is electricity?

3. What are the moving charges in a metallic substance that is conducting electricity? What are the moving charges in a solution that is conducting electricity?

4. Write the 2 different equations that are typically used to show the self-ionization of water. Which equation is the "correct" one that should always be used? State one argument in favor of using each of the equations.

5. What is the correct equilibrium constant expression for the ionization of water? What is the numerical value for this equilibrium constant at 25°C? What symbol and name are given to this expression?

6. Select all the true statements from among the following. (It is assumed that the temperature is 25°C.)

    A. The product of the hydrogen ion and hydroxide ion concentrations in pure water must equal 1.00×10^{-14}.

    B. In pure water the concentration of the hydrogen ion and hydroxide ion will be equal.

    C. In pure water the concentration of the hydrogen ion will be equal to 10^{-7} M.

    D. In pure water the concentration of the hydroxide ion will be equal to 10^{-7} M.

    E. The product of the hydrogen ion and hydroxide ion concentrations in any aqueous solution must equal 1.00×10^{-14}.

    F. If an aqueous solution has a hydrogen ion concentration of 10^{-7} M, then the hydroxide ion concentration must also equal 10^{-7} M.

    G. If the hydrogen ion concentration in an aqueous solution is greater than 10^{-7} M, then the hydroxide ion concentration must also be greater than 10^{-7} M.

    H. If the hydrogen ion concentration in an aqueous solution is greater than 10^{-7} M, then the hydroxide ion concentration must be less than 10^{-7} M.

7. What is the hydroxide ion concentration in a solution that has a hydrogen ion concentration equal to 10^{-9} M?

8. What is the hydrogen ion concentration in a solution with a hydroxide ion concentration of 9.2×10^{-3} M?

9. If the concentration of hydroxide ion in an aqueous solution equals 7.8×10^{-4} M, what is the concentration of hydrogen ion in the same solution?

Advanced Problems

10. An aqueous solution has a hydrogen ion concentration that is 3 times the concentration of hydroxide ion concentration in the same solution. What are the concentrations of both ions?

11. At 30°C, K_w is equal to 1.471×10^{-14}.

    A. What would be the concentration of H^+ and OH^- in an aqueous solution at this temperature?

    B. What would be the pH of water at this temperature?

    C. Is pure water acidic, basic, or neutral at this temperature? Explain.

Lecture Twenty-Nine
Strong Acids and Bases—General Properties

Scope:

We will now broaden our understanding of pH by examining strong acids and bases. The term "strong" does not describe the concentration of a solution but rather how highly the substance is ionized in solution. We will apply what we have learned by finding some pH-related values in solutions of strong acids.

Outline

I. In this lecture we continue our study of the meaning and usefulness of the concept of pH.

    A. The pH of a solution can be found if the $[H^+]$ in the solution is known, since $pH = -\log[H^+]$.

    B. It is also possible to find the $[H^+]$ in a solution if the pH is known, since $[H^+] = 10^{-pH}$.

    C. Another quantity that can be specified for a solution is its pOH.

        1. The pOH of a solution is equal to $-\log[OH^-]$.

        2. The sum of the pH and the pOH of a solution equals 14.

II. A strong acid or base is defined as an acid or base that is 100% ionized in solution.

    A. The term "strength" is not related to the concentration of the solution.

        1. Strength refers only to how highly ionized the substance is, not how concentrated the solution is or how dangerous the solution might be.

        2. It is quite common to confuse the terms "strength" and "concentration."

    B. There are 6 common strong acids in nature: HCl, HBr, HI, HNO_3, $HClO_4$, and H_2SO_4.

        1. These acids are 100% ionized in solution.

        2. Sulfuric acid ionizes one H^+ at a time and is a strong acid only for the first ionization.

III. An introductory problem is worked involving finding the concentrations of H^+ and OH^-, the pH, and the pOH in solutions of strong acids.

Lecture Twenty-Nine—Questions
Strong Acids and Bases—General Properties

Standard Problems

1. What is the pH of a solution with a $[H^+] = 3.74 \times 10^{-12}$ M?

2. What is the pH of a solution with a hydroxide ion concentration of 5.87×10^{-6} M?

3. What is $[H^+]$ in a solution with a pH $= 13$?

4. What is $[H^+]$ in a solution with a pH $= 7.49$?

5. What is the pOH of a solution with a hydrogen ion concentration of 4.84×10^{-8} M?

6. How did we define an acid and base in these lectures?

7. What is meant by the term "strong acid"?

8. Are most acids strong or weak?

9. Give the names and formulas for 6 common strong acids.

10. Suppose we discovered a new strong acid with the formula $HMwO_5$. Write the equation that would represent its ionization.

Lecture Thirty
Solving Strong Acid and Base Problems

Scope:

In this lecture we finish our segment on strong acids and bases by working some additional practice problems. A solid knowledge of strong acids and bases is critical because nearly all bases encountered in introductory chemistry classes are strong bases.

Outline

I. Additional strong acid problems are worked to begin this lecture.

II. Almost all bases encountered in a first-year chemistry course are strong bases.

    A. All bases that contain a metallic ion are strong bases.

    B. When a strong base contains more than 1 hydroxide group, they all ionize at once, instead of in steps.

    C. Several problems involving solutions of strong bases are presented and solved.

Lecture Thirty—Questions
Solving Strong Acid and Base Problems

Standard Problems

1. If 5.28 g HCl were dissolved in 396 mL solution, what would be the $[H^+]$, $[OH^-]$, pH, and pOH of this solution?

2. If 23.83 g HNO_3 were dissolved in 5.24 L solution, what would be the $[H^+]$, $[OH^-]$, pH, and pOH of this solution?

3. Are most bases strong or weak?

4. What type of compounds are most of the bases encountered in a high school chemistry course?

5. Write equations for the dissolving of each of the following bases in water.

   A. LiOH

   B. $Ca(OH)_2$

6. Name 2 chemical families for which you can determine the charge on the metallic ion in a metallic hydroxide. List the elements that belong in each of these families and what their charges would be.

7. If 9.16 g NaOH were dissolved in 582 mL solution, what would be the $[H^+]$, $[OH^-]$, pH, and pOH of the solution?

8. Calculate the pH of a solution prepared by dissolving 7.77 g $Ba(OH)_2$ in 777 mL solution.

Advanced Problem

9. Calculate the pH of a solution prepared by mixing 38.00 mL of 1.22 M HCl with 45.00 mL of 1.44 M NaOH. The chemical reaction that takes place is $H^+ + OH^- \leftrightarrow H_2O$.

Lecture Thirty-One
Weak Acids and Bases

Scope:

We now look at weak acids and bases, those that are only slightly ionized in water-based solutions. While many bases are strong, most acids are weak. In this lecture we will learn how to solve the classic weak acid problem—determining the concentrations, pH, pOH, and ionization level in a solution of weak acid. Once we are able to solve weak acid problems, we can use the same approach for weak base problems.

Outline

I. Weak acids are acids that are only slightly ionized in aqueous solution.

  A. They can be contrasted with the 6 common strong acids, which are essentially 100% ionized in aqueous solution.

  B. Most acids are weak acids.

  C. Weak acids still differ from each other in their relative strengths.

  1. The best way to compare the relative strengths of weak acids is to compare the numerical value for their ionization constants, K_a.

  a. For a general weak acid HX, $K_a = [H^+][X^-]/[HX]$.

  b. The smaller the numerical value of K_a, the weaker the acid.

  2. Chemists have prepared and published tables that compare the relative strengths of acids according to the numerical values for their ionization constants.

  D. The classic weak acid problem involves determining the concentrations of all molecular and ionic species, the pH, the pOH, and the percent ionization in a solution of a weak acid of known concentration.

II. Several weak acid problems are presented and solved.

III. Weak base problems can be solved in the same manner as weak acid problems.

  A. The only common weak base generally encountered in a first-year high school chemistry course is ammonia, NH_3.

  1. Ammonia ionizes according to the equation $NH_3 + H_2O \leftrightarrow NH_4^+ + OH^-$.

  2. The ionization constant (K_b) for ammonia is 1.8×10^{-5}.

  B. When solving problems involving solutions of ammonia, you should remember that the x that is solved for represents the concentration of hydroxide ion, not hydrogen ion.

Lecture Thirty-One—Questions
Weak Acids and Bases

Standard Problems

1. Write the equation for the ionization of the weak acid $HClO_2$ and the expression for its equilibrium constant.

2. How do you know that the K_a for any weak acid is a small number?

3. Imagine that 1.00 M solutions of the following acids are prepared. Arrange the acid solutions in order of pH, from the lowest to the highest. Use the table of K_a values included in the appendices (under "Ionization Constants") to help you arrive at your answer.

   HF, HCN, HCl, HNO_2, $HC_2H_3O_2$, HSO_4^-

4. Determine the concentrations of H^+, BrO^-, $HBrO$, and OH^- and the pH, pOH, and percent ionization in a 1.00 M solution of hypobromous acid ($HBrO$, $K_a = 2.5 \times 10^{-9}$).

5. Determine the concentrations of H^+, OCN^-, $HOCN$, and OH^- and the pH, pOH, and percent ionization in a 0.75 M solution of cyanic acid ($HOCN$, $K_a = 3.5 \times 10^{-4}$).

6. Ammonia is a weak base that ionizes as follows:

   $$NH_3 + H_2O \leftrightarrow NH_4^+ + OH^-$$

   If the K_b for ammonia is 1.8×10^{-5}, what would be the pH and the percent ionization in a 0.370 M solution of NH_3?

Advanced Problem

7. A solution is prepared by mixing 500 mL of 1.00 M HCl with 500 mL of 1.00 M $HC_2H_3O_2$. What is the pH of the mixed solution? K_a for $HC_2H_3O_2 = 1.8 \times 10^{-5}$.

Lecture Thirty-Two
Titrating Acids and Bases

Scope:

Acids and bases neutralize each other, and these neutralization reactions can be used in laboratory procedures called titrations. In this lecture we learn how to perform titrations and how to use them to determine unknown concentrations of acids and bases.

Outline

I. Acids and bases neutralize each other. Hydrogen ions and hydroxide ions tend to combine to form water.

II. Reactions between strong acids and strong bases have extremely large equilibrium expressions. These reactions essentially go to completion to form water.

III. Neutralization reactions are used in laboratory procedures called titrations. A titration allows us to determine the unknown concentration of an acid or base.

    A. Titrations have 2 key requirements.
        1. The amounts of acid and base mixed together must be carefully controlled and measured.
        2. There must be some way of determining when enough acid or base has been added to neutralize the solution.

    B. The equivalence point is the point at which enough acid or base has been added to neutralize the solution.

    C. A pH meter or acid-base indicator can be used to determine when the equivalence point has been reached.

    D. Titrations are performed by using burettes, which allow you to carefully control and measure the amounts of acid and base mixed together.

    E. Solutions of unknown concentrations are mixed with standard solutions of known concentrations. The number of moles used from the standard solution can be related to the number of moles of the unknown. Molarity can then be calculated from this information.

IV. The rest of the lecture is devoted to describing the titration procedure and solving sample problems.

Lecture Thirty-Two—Questions
Titrating Acids and Bases

Standard Problems

1. What allows us to say, for all practical purposes, that the reaction of a strong acid with a strong base essentially goes to completion?

2. What is the technical difference between the equivalence point of a titration and the end point?

3. Why can the end point in a titration be assumed to be an adequate approximation of the actual equivalence point?

4. What are we using as our preliminary definition of an indicator? Name 2 indicators commonly used in high school labs and state their colors in acidic and basic solutions.

5. Explain why each of these procedures is performed during an acid-base titration lab. Assume you are going to determine the concentration of an unknown acid by titrating it with a solution of a standardized base.

   A. After cleaning the burettes, some of the solutions they are going to be filled with are added to the burettes and rolled around inside them, and then this solution is discarded.

   B. After filling your burettes, you drain a bit of the acid or base into a waste container and discard it.

   C. After adding your acid solution to the reaction vessel, you add an unmeasured amount of distilled water to the reaction vessel.

   D. You constantly swirl the solution in the reaction vessel as you perform the titration.

   E. If you accidentally add too much base, and the solution turns more red than pink, suggesting that you have gone past the end point, additional acid is then added drop by drop until a good end point is achieved. If you accidentally go past the end point when trying to add more acid, then additional base is added drop by drop until a good end point is achieved.

6. A titration is performed by adding a standardized solution of NaOH to a solution of an unknown solution of HCl. The following data is obtained.

   Initial reading of acid burette: 1.55 mL

   Initial reading of base burette: 0.75 mL

   Final reading of acid burette: 44.25 mL

   Final reading of base burette: 32.50 mL

   Concentration of standard base solution: 0.383 M

   A. Is the concentration of the unknown acid greater than or less than 0.383 M?

   B. Calculate the concentration of the unknown acid.

Advanced Problems

7. A student titrates an unknown solution of H_2SO_4 with a standard solution of NaOH. The following data are obtained.

    Initial reading of acid burette: 0.15 mL

    Initial reading of base burette: 1.05 mL

    Final reading of acid burette: 22.25 mL

    Final reading of base burette: 46.50 mL

    Concentration of standard base solution: 0.558 M

    Calculate the concentration of the unknown acid solution. Hint: Think carefully about the equation for the reaction before you do the calculations.

8. A very popular formula for solving acid-base titration problems is $M_aV_a = M_bV_b$, where M_a is the molarity of the unknown acid, V_a is the volume of the unknown acid, and M_b and V_b are corresponding terms for the base.

    A. Why does this formula work?

    B. Under what circumstances would the formula not work?

    C. Why do you think this formula was not presented in this lecture?

Lecture Thirty-Three
Titration Curves and Indicators

Scope:

In this lecture we discover how acid-base indicators can be used to find the equivalence point of a titration. These acid-base indicators reveal by their colors whether a solution is acidic or basic. Since pH changes drastically near the equivalence point, testing the pH with acid-base indicators can tell us when a solution has reached the equivalence point and whether the resulting solution is acidic, basic, or neutral.

Outline

I. Acid-base indicators are used to determine the equivalence point of a titration.

    A. The pH of the unknown solution changes dramatically around the equivalence point.

    B. Acid-base indicators measure pH changes, so they change color quickly at the equivalence point.

II. Acid-base indicators are one color in an acidic solution and a different color in a basic solution. More specifically, an acid-base indicator is a weak acid or base whose molecular form is one color while its ionic form is another.

    A. Indicators ionize to a certain extent in solution, which can be measured by an ionization constant.

    B. A weak acid indicator will change color when the pH of the solution into which it is placed equals pK_a for the indicator ($pK_a = -\log K_a$).

    C. Indicators come in a variety of colors and operate in different pH ranges. The indicator chosen for a particular titration will depend on the pH range of the solution at the equivalence point.

III. Titrations can result in acidic, basic, or neutral solutions at the equivalence point.

    A. Strong acids titrated with strong bases result in neutral solutions at the equivalence point.

    B. Weak acids titrated with strong bases result in basic solutions at the equivalence point.

    C. Strong acids titrated with weak bases result in acidic solutions at the equivalence point.

IV. Titration curves for weak acids and strong bases differ from strong acid/strong base titration curves.

    A. The initial pH is higher in weak acid/strong base titrations.

    B. The pH does not jump as dramatically around the equivalence point for weak acid/strong base titrations.

    C. The pH at the equivalence point is above 7 for weak acid/strong base titrations.

Lecture Thirty-Three—Questions
Titration Curves and Indicators

Standard Problems

1. Consider the titration curve for titrating a strong acid, like HCl, with a strong base, like NaOH. Select all the true statements from among the following.

    A. At the beginning of the titration, the pH of the solution is 7.

    B. At the beginning of the titration, the pH of the solution will be below 7.

    C. At first the pH of the solution rises rapidly as base is added.

    D. The pH of the solution rises at a constant rate as base is added.

    E. At the equivalence point of the titration, the pH of the solution is 7.

    F. The pH of the solution changes very rapidly around the equivalence point of the titration.

    G. When you get well past the equivalence point, the pH of the solution rises rapidly.

    H. After you pass the equivalence point, the pH of the solution will be greater than 7.

    I. Any indicator that changes color from perhaps a pH of 4 to a pH of 10 would be appropriate to use in this titration.

2. What is a good definition of an indicator?

3. Do indicators have some special property that causes them to change color so rapidly around the equivalence point of a titration? If so, what is this property? If not, why do they change color so rapidly?

4. Consider weak acid indicators. Why do different indicators change color over different pH ranges?

5. Suppose a weak acid indicator had a $K_a = 8.3 \times 10^{-6}$. Around what pH would you expect it to change color?

6. What was the comical "ME STRONG ACID; me weak base" joke designed to help you remember?

7. From the following lists, select the indicator that would be most appropriate for each of the titrations listed.

    Titrations:

    A. 1.00 M HNO_3 titrated with 1.00 M NaOH

    B. 1.00 M $HC_2H_3O_2$ with 1.00 M KOH.

    C. 1.00 M NH_3 with 1.00 M HCl.

    Indicators:

    a. methyl red: changes color from pH 4.4–6.2

    b. litmus: changes color from pH 5–8

    c. alizarin yellow: changes color from 10.0–12.0

8. Two students are assigned to do 2 different titrations and prepare titration curves. Student A is told to titrate 50.0 mL of 1.00 M HCl, a strong acid, with 1.00 M NaOH, a strong base. Student B is told to titrate 50.0 mL of 1.00 M HClO, a weak acid, with 1.00 M NaOH. Student A correctly calculates that he needs 50.0 mL of 1.00 M NaOH to complete his titration. When the 2 students go to the stock room, they find that there is only a total of 70.0 mL of the 1.00 M NaOH available for both of them. Student B suggests that they both should just titrate 25.00 mL of their acids with the NaOH, arguing that both of them will then require only 25.0 mL of the NaOH, so there will be enough for both of them to complete their projects. Student A argues that he should get 50.0 mL of the NaOH, since that is how much he needs, and anyway, the remaining 20.0 mL should be more than enough for Student B, since he is titrating a weak acid and since weak acids only contain a small concentration of H^+, so he will not really need much of the NaOH to complete his project. Which is the better plan? Explain why.

9. Suppose you were to titrate a 1.00 M solution of a weak acid like acetic acid ($HC_2H_3O_2$) with a strong base like KOH. Select all of the true statements from among the following.

   A. The pH of the initial acid solution would be the same as it would be if your starting solution was 1.00 M HCl, since both are 1.00 M solutions.

   B. The pH would still rise slowly at the beginning of the titration.

   C. The pH at the equivalence point would be below 7.

   D. The pH at the equivalence point would be greater than 7.

   E. The pH at the equivalence point rises just as much and just as rapidly as it did when we titrated HCl with NaOH.

   F. The pH at the equivalence point rises rapidly, but not quite as much as it did when we titrated HCl with NaOH.

Advanced Problem

10. A lab assistant is given the assignment of standardizing the solution of NaOH that is to be used in a titration lab. To do this, he carefully weighs out 2.878 g solid potassium hydrogen phthalate ($KHC_8H_4O_4$, often abbreviated as KHP in laboratory manuals), dissolves it in some distilled water, and titrates it with the solution of NaOH that is to be standardized. He determines that it takes 23.65 mL of the base to just neutralize the sample of KHP. Given that the equation for the reaction that occurred was

$$HC_8H_4O_4^- + OH^- \leftrightarrow H_2O + C_8H_4O_4^{2-}$$

calculate the concentration of the solution of base.

Lecture Thirty-Four
Solubility Equilibria—Principles, Problems

Scope:

This lecture introduces us to solubility equilibria, the equilibria found in saturated solutions of slightly soluble ionic solids. We will discuss the difference between dissociation equilibria and solubility equilibria, and we will clarify some possible points of confusion in solving solubility equilibria problems.

Outline

I. The term "solubility equilibria" refers to the kind of equilibria that exist in saturated solutions of slightly soluble ionic solids.

    A. A classic example would be the equilibrium that exists in a saturated solution of silver chloride (AgCl).

        1. This equilibrium can be represented by the equation $AgCl(s) \leftrightarrow Ag^+ + Cl^-$.

        2. The equilibrium constant for a system is given the symbol K_{sp} and is referred to as a solubility product.

            a. For this system, $K_{sp} = [Ag^+][Cl^-]$.

            b. There is no denominator in the expression for the solubility product because the denominator is a pure solid, and pure solids and liquids are never included in equilibrium constant expressions.

    B. One important difference between dissociation equilibria and solubility equilibria is that in a dissociation equilibrium the value of the equilibrium constant must always be satisfied, whereas in a solubility equilibrium the solubility product is only satisfied if the solution is saturated.

    C. In these types of equilibria, it is important to not confuse the molar solubility of the substance with the value of its solubility product.

        1. The term "solubility" refers to how much of a substance can be dissolved in a liter of solution, i.e., the molarity of a saturated solution.

        2. The term "solubility product" refers to the numerical value of the equilibrium constant for the equation that represents the substance dissolving in water.

        3. For example, the solubility of AgCl in water is about 1.3×10^{-5} M, whereas the value of the solubility product is 1.8×10^{-10}.

        4. Two classic types of problems are to determine the molar solubility of an ionic solid given the value of this solubility product, and vice versa.

II. In this lecture several problems relating to the solubility and the solubility product of various ionic solids are presented and solved.

Lecture Thirty-Four—Questions
Solubility Equilibria—Principles, Problems

Standard Problems

1. What is 1 critical difference between solubility equilibria and the other kinds of equilibrium systems we have been discussing, such as the equilibria that exist in solutions of weak acids?

2. Write the correct solubility product expressions for each of the following solubility equilibria.

    A. $AgI(s) \leftrightarrow Ag^+ + I^-$

    B. $CaSO_4(s) \leftrightarrow Ca^{2+} + SO_4^{2-}$

    C. $Ag_2CO_3(s) \leftrightarrow 2Ag^+ + CO_3^{2-}$

    D. $Li_3PO_4(s) \leftrightarrow 3Li^+ + PO_4^{3-}$

    E. $Hg_2Cl_2(s) \leftrightarrow Hg_2^{2+} + 2Cl^-$

    F. $Sr_3(AsO_4)_2(s) \leftrightarrow 3Sr^{2+} + 2AsO_4^{3-}$

3. Distinguish between the terms "solubility" and "solubility product."

4. Calculate the molar solubility of $PbSO_4$, given that its solubility product equals 1.6×10^{-8}. The 2 ions formed when it dissolves in water are Pb^{2+} and SO_4^{2-}.

5. Calculate the molar solubility of $Fe(OH)_3$, given that its solubility product equals 4×10^{-38}.

6. Calculate the molar solubility of $Sr_3(AsO_4)_2$, given that its solubility product equals 4.29×10^{-19}.

7. Given that the molar solubility of $BaSO_4$ is equal to 1.05×10^{-5} M, calculate its solubility product.

8. Given that the molar solubility of Ag_2CO_3 is equal to 1.27×10^{-4} M, calculate its solubility product.

Advanced Problems

9. Consider a hypothetical compound with the formula M_3X_4 that dissolves to produce M^{4+} and X^{3-} ions in solution. If the solubility product of this compound equals 8.2×10^{-24}, calculate the compound's molar solubility.

10. Consider 2 compounds, A and B. A has a solubility product of 3.3×10^{-5}, while B has a solubility product of 4.4×10^{-7}. Can we conclude that compound A has a higher molar solubility than compound B?

Lecture Thirty-Five
Solubility Equilibria—Common Ion Effect

Scope:

Our study of solubility equilibria continues with some more advanced practice problems. In this lecture, we encounter the last major type of equilibrium problem that we will see in this course: those that involve the effect of already-present solutes on the solubility of an added ionic solid. In solving this problem, we will revisit Le Chatelier's principle and will learn some pitfalls to beware of when calculating the equations.

Outline

I. We start this lecture by tackling a fairly involved solubility problem that probably exceeds what is demanded in most high school courses but will provide a good vehicle to sharpen our reasoning skills even further.

II. Next we encounter the last general type of equilibrium problem in this course. These problems involve situations where a slightly soluble ionic solid is establishing an equilibrium with a solution that happens to contain a second source of one of the ions present in that equilibrium.

   A. This problem shows that the solubility of a substance can be markedly affected by the presence of other solutes in the solution.

   B. This is in fact predicted by Le Chatelier's principle, which we learned several lectures ago.

III. In our last practice problem, we have to combine the processes developed in this lecture with concepts and processes learned earlier in the course.

Lecture Thirty-Five—Questions
Solubility Equilibria—Common Ion Effect

Standard Problems

1. Explain what is meant by the phrase "common ion effect" and how this effect can be accounted for by applying Le Chatelier's principle.

2. The K_{sp} of $PbSO_4$ is 1.6×10^{-8}.
   A. Calculate the solubility of $PbSO_4$ in a 0.25 M solution of $Pb(NO_3)_2$.
   B. How does this answer compare to the solubility of $PbSO_4$ in pure water, which you calculated in question 4 of Lecture Thirty-Four?

3. The K_{sp} of $Ca(OH)_2$ is 5.5×10^{-6}.
   A. Calculate the solubility of $Ca(OH)_2$ in pure water.
   B. Calculate the solubility of $Ca(OH)_2$ in a 0.77 M solution of $Ba(OH)_2$.

4. The K_{sp} of $Mg(OH)_2$ is 1.8×10^{-11}.
   A. Calculate the solubility of $Mg(OH)_2$ in pure water.
   B. Calculate the molar solubility of $Mg(OH)_2$ in a solution with a pH of 11.22.

Advanced Problems

5. The solubility product of Bi_2S_3 is listed as an unimaginably small number, 1×10^{-97}.
   A. Calculate the solubility of Bi_2S_3 in pure water.

   Suppose you tried to dissolve some Bi_2S_3 in a solution of 0.50 M Na_2S.
   B. How many grams of Bi_2S_3 would theoretically dissolve in 1 L of this solution?
   C. How many formula units of Bi_2S_3 would theoretically dissolve in 1 L of this solution?
   D. How many liters of this solution would it theoretically take to dissolve 1.00 g Bi_2S_3?

Lecture Thirty-Six
Putting It All Together

Scope:

In the final lecture, we will solve problems that require pulling together all of the knowledge that we have acquired throughout the course. To avoid the dull nature of review problems, I have included in each of these final exercises an element that is completely new but entirely workable within the logical framework that we have built. These problems are meant to be challenging—their primary goal is to build confidence in your ability to encounter and unravel new problems. With that confidence and with the deep understanding of chemistry that this course has emphasized, any student should feel well equipped to tackle even higher levels of learning in chemistry.

Outline

I.   This lecture pulls together concepts and skills learned from previous lectures and asks you to solve challenging problems that you have not encountered before.

II. The first problem pulls together concepts of molar volume, molarity, acid strength, stoichiometry, pH, and pOH.

III. The second problem pulls together the concepts of balancing chemical equations, solubility products, stoichiometry, molar mass, and molarity.

IV. The final problem pulls together concepts of stoichiometry, pH, and ionization constants.

Lecture Thirty-Six—Questions
Putting It All Together

Note: The best review approach may very well be to simply rework the workbook problems from each lecture that you have worked in the past, as it is highly unlikely that you would remember the actual solutions. But here are several additional review items.

1. How many molecules are contained in 9.29 L SO_2 gas at STP? How many grams of sulfur dioxide would be contained in this volume?

2. A compound consists of 62.62% Ba, 22.78% As, and 14.60% O. What is the empirical formula of the compound?

3. Consider this balanced chemical equation:

    $2K_2CrO_4 + 6NaCl + 16HClO_4 \rightarrow 3Cl_2(g) + 2Cr(ClO_4)_3 + 6NaClO_4 + 4KClO_4 + 8H_2O + 277$ kJ

    A. How many grams of $HClO_4$ are required to produce 22.35 g $Cr(ClO_4)_3$?

    B. How many liters of Cl_2 gas at STP are produced along with 8.22 g H_2O?

    C. How many molecules of water will be produced if 132 kJ of energy are released in the reaction?

    D. How many molecules of $HClO_4$ are needed to react with 8.26×10^{21} formula units of NaCl?

    E. Suppose 235.0 g K_2CrO_4 were reacted with 235.0 g NaCl.
        i. Which reactant is the limiting reactant? Show calculations that support your conclusion.
        ii. How many grams of $NaClO_4$ could be produced?
        iii. How many grams of the excess reactant would remain when the reaction was complete?

4. Consider this equilibrium system:

    $2C_6H_6(g) + 15O_2(g) \leftrightarrow 12CO_2(g) + 6H_2O(g)$, $\Delta H = -6340$ kJ

    A. If C_6H_6 were removed from this system …
        i. Which way would the system shift?
        ii. What would happen to the concentration of each reactant and product?
        iii. What would happen to the numerical value for K?

    B. If the temperature of this system were raised …
        i. Which way would the system shift?
        ii. What would happen to the concentration of each reactant and product?
        iii. What would happen to the numerical value for K?

    C. If the pressure of this system were decreased …
        i. Which way would the system shift?
        ii. What would happen to the amount of each reactant and product?
        iii. What would happen to the numerical value for K?

5. What is the molarity of a solution prepared by dissolving 45.28 g $Al(NO_3)_3$ in water to produce 628.0 mL solution? What are the concentrations of both the aluminum ion and chloride ion in this solution?

6. Consider this chemical reaction:

    $SO_2Cl_2(g) + 8HBr(aq) \rightarrow H_2S(g) + 2HCl(aq) + 4Br_2(l) + 2H_2O(l)$

    How many milliliters of a 3.50 M solution of HBr are required to react with 7.33 L SO_2Cl_2 gas at STP?

7. Consider this equilibrium system:

$$Ca_3(PO_4)_2(s) \leftrightarrow 3Ca^{2+}(aq) + 2PO_4^{3-}(aq)$$

If some solid, soluble $Ca(NO_3)_2$ were dissolved into this system …
A. Which way would the system shift?
B. What would happen to both the amount and concentration of each reactant and product?

8. Consider this equilibrium system for butyric acid:

$$HC_4H_7O_2 \leftrightarrow H^+ + C_4H_7O_2^-, K_a = 1.5 \times 10^{-5}$$

Calculate the concentrations of $HC_4H_7O_2$, H^+, $C_4H_7O_2^-$, and OH^-; the pH, the pOH, and the percent ionization in a 0.44 M solution of butyric acid.

9. How many grams of MgF_2 can be dissolved into 250 mL of 0.666 M KF if K_{sp} for MgF_2 is equal to 3.7×10^{-8}?

10. Calculate the molar solubility of $Ba(IO_3)_2$, given that its K_{sp} is equal to 1.5×10^{-9}.

11. Consider this hypothetical equilibrium system:

$$2A + B \leftrightarrow C + 3D$$

When 1.30 mol A and 2.20 mol B are placed in a 1.00-L container and are allowed to establish equilibrium, the concentration of C is measured and found to be 0.38 M. Calculate the numerical value for the equilibrium constant for this reaction.

12. Consider this hypothetical equilibrium system:

$$A + 3B \leftrightarrow 2C + D$$

When 1.75 mol A, 2.75 mol B, and 0.65 mol C are placed in a 1.00-L container and allowed to establish equilibrium, the concentration of A is measured and found to be 1.26 M. Calculate the numerical value for the equilibrium constant for this reaction.

13. How many protons, electrons, and neutrons are there in each of the following?
A. $^{137}_{56}Ba^{2+}$
B. $^{128}_{52}Te^{2-}$
C. $^{251}_{98}Cf$

14. Which family of elements has each of the following general properties?
A. Represents the most unreactive of all the chemical families.
B. Are the most chemically reactive family of metallic elements.
C. Are highly reactive nonmetals that exist as diatomic elements.
D. Are a main-group family that forms +2 ions.
E. Form many molecular compounds, but also form ionic compounds, where they often exist as anions with a −2 charge.

15. Liquid mercury has a density of 13.6 g/mL. How many mercury atoms are contained in a 7.00-mL sample of liquid mercury?

16. Balance each of the following chemical equations:

   A. $Ca_3(PO_4)_2 + SiO_2 \leftrightarrow P_2O_5 + CaSiO_3$

   B. $CuCl + HCl \leftrightarrow CuCl_2 + H_2O$

   C. $B_2O_3 + C \leftrightarrow B_4C + CO$

   D. $H_3N + O_2 \leftrightarrow N_2 + H_2O$

   E. $NO_2 + H_2O \leftrightarrow HNO_3 + NO$

   F. $NaOH + Cl_2 \leftrightarrow NaClO_3 + NaCl + H_2O$ (There is hint below if you want one.)

   Hint: Leave Cl_2 until the end (free element). Start by trying to determine which coefficients are needed to balance the oxygen and hydrogen. This is a difficult equation.

17. An experiment calls for 7.83 g NaOH. How many milliliters of a 0.72 M solution are required?

18. Consider this reaction:

   $3SnCl_4(aq) + 4K_3PO_4(aq) \rightarrow 12KCl(aq) + Sn_3(PO_4)_4(s)$

   Suppose 225 mL of a 1.85 M solution of $SnCl_4$ is mixed with 350 mL of a 1.77 M solution of K_3PO_4.

   A. Which substance is the limiting reactant? Show calculations that support your conclusion.

   B. How many grams of $Sn_3(PO_4)_4$ would be produced?

Workbook Answers

Lecture One
Introduction and Philosophy

1. D

2. False. Solving most high school chemistry problems only involves applying quantitative reasoning that you use easily and naturally in your everyday life.

3. A self-fulfilling prophesy is a prophesy that comes true solely because people believe it will come true. The example given in the lecture is a bank that fails for no other reason than the fact that people believe it is going to fail: This belief causes them to withdraw their money—what is called a run on a bank. The bank fails even though it is a very sound bank. The belief that it was going to fail caused it to fail. Similarly, some chemistry students who believe that they will not do well in chemistry become so negative in their attitudes and nervous at the first sign of difficulty that their very belief that they will not do well results in their not doing well.

4. The quantitative thinking that is applied when solving a problem like the students and rooms problem is identical to the kind of quantitative thinking required to solve most high school chemistry problems. Solving this problem correctly demonstrates that you have the requisite ability to solve high school chemistry problems.

5. The numbers encountered in chemistry problems are not always nice, whole numbers. They often involve decimals and exponential numbers, which some students find more difficult to reason with. Also, students may not have a deep understanding of what the numbers given in a problem really represent; without this understanding, they do not know how to reason through the problem.

6. It is not necessary to view all the lectures in order. It is recommended that the first 4 lectures be viewed in order and mastered before continuing. After that, students can view whichever lecture or lectures might relate to whatever they are studying in class at that particular time.

7. Go back and view the lecture or lectures that apply to the topic that you either have not been exposed to or have forgotten.

8. Try to solve every problem before watching the solution on the video. Be an active learner, not a passive observer.

9. Starting with 0, then 1, each successive number in the sequence is obtained by adding the previous 2 numbers. This is a very famous sequence called the Fibonacci numbers.

Lecture Two
Basic Concepts of Quantitative Reasoning

1. Amounts and this per thats

2. **A.** This per that

   B. This per that

   C. Amount

   D. Amount

   E. This per that

   F. Neither. Although this is a fraction, the denominator is not a single quantity. The denominator itself is a this per that.

   G. Amount

3. The 3 techniques are (1) use of a formula or equation, (2) the proportion method, and (3) the factor-label method.

4. Plugging numbers into a formula allows you to solve a problem without really understanding the underlying concepts. As the number of different formulas increases, it becomes more and more difficult to both remember them and know where and when they can be applied.

5. Because these 2 approaches can be applied without a real understanding of the nature of the actual quantities that appear in a problem or the concepts that underlie the problem. When problems become more complex, this lack of fundamental understanding can cause serious difficulties that are not easily remedied.

6. First, try to understand what the numbers given in the problem are really representing. Second, try to visualize what is being described in the problem. Third, try to put the quantities together in the natural way they would have to go together to make any sense.

7. You can check your answer by using a formula, proportions, or the factor-label approach, but these should be used to check your work, not as the primary approaches to obtaining the solution to the problem.

8. They do not really understand what the numbers given in the problem truly represent.

Lecture Three
Quantitative Reasoning in Everyday Life

1. It tells you how many you have of whatever is in the numerator for 1 of what is in the denominator.

2. It tells you how many miles you can drive in 1 h.

3. Although this fraction certainly tells you that you can drive 238 mi in 4.5 h, what it is really telling you (i.e., the way you should think about this) is how many miles you can drive in 1 h. If you actually do the division, it says that you can drive $\frac{238 \text{ mi}}{4.5 \text{ h}}$, or 52.9 mi/h.

4. The number of gallons of gas it takes to drive 1 mi is a this per that. The "this" is the number of gallons of gas you use; the "that" is the number of miles you drive. This car uses 1 gal gas to go 48 mi, so the gallons per mile would be $\frac{1 \text{ gal}}{48 \text{ mi}}$, or 0.021 gal/mi. It takes much less than 1 gal to drive just 1 mi, which makes sense.

5. Cover up the numbers. Just look at the units. Without the numbers this is easier to see. Miles per hour tells you how many miles you can drive in 1 h. Gallons per mile tells you how many gallons of gas it takes to drive 1 mi.

6. Read the problem several times, both rapidly and slowly; stop to think; and visualize. Then draw a picture of the things being described in the problem. Attach proper units to all numbers given in the problem, and think about what these numbers represent.

7. (6 mo)(30.5 days/mo) = 183 days

   (183 days)(8.5 mi/day) = 1555 mi

8. $\frac{5 \text{ mi}}{47 \text{ mi/h}}$ = 0.164 h

   Note: A common error here would be to divide 47 by 5, but it is very unlikely that you would do this if you stopped and visualized a distance of 5 mi and a car that was traveling at 47 mi/h. Stopping to think about this would make it clear that it would take much less than 1 h to travel the 5 mi.

   (0.1064 h)(60 min/h)(60 s/min) = 383 s

9. $\frac{\$11.85}{\$6.99/\text{lb}}$ = 1.70 lb

10. $\frac{825 \text{ mi}}{29.7 \text{ mi/gal}}$ = 27.78 gal

    (27.78 gal)($4.28/gal) = $118.90

11. (87 students)(120 M&M's/student) = 10,440 M&M's

    (10,440 M&M's)(0.89 g/M&M) = 9291.6 g M&M's

    $\frac{9291.6 \text{ g}}{100 \text{ g/package}}$ = 93 packages (since you cannot purchase a fraction of a package)

Lecture Four
Quantitative Reasoning in Chemistry—Density

1. Mass refers to how much matter the object contains.

2. Volume refers to how much space is taken up by the object.

3. Density refers to how much mass is contained in a given volume of a substance.

4. F; both B and C are correct.

5. The density is 5.00 g/cm^3. Density does not depend on how much of the material you have; 2.00 cm^3 would have a mass of 10.00 g, but the density would still be 5.00 g/cm^3: $\frac{10.00 \text{ g}}{2.00 \text{ cm}^3}$ = 5.00 g/cm^3.

6. Dime, nickel, small fork, orange, liter bottle of soda

7. $\frac{6.25 \text{ g}}{7.34 \text{ cm}^3}$ = 0.851 g/cm^3

8. (1.44 g/cm^3)(8.29 cm^3) = 11.94 g

9. $\frac{9.00 \text{ g}}{13.59 \text{ g/cm}^3}$ = 0.662 cm^3. Did you reason that the volume had to be less than 1 cm^3 before you did the math?

10. This problem illustrates how to determine the volume of an irregularly shaped object by using the technique of water displacement: volume of object = (final water level) − (initial water level).

    volume = 44.8 − 35.2 = 9.6 cm^3

    density = $\frac{28.73 \text{ g}}{9.6 \text{ cm}^3}$ = 2.99 g/cm^3

11. The Nerf ball. Even though it has less mass, its low density (Nerf balls are made of a low-density, spongelike material) means that the Nerf ball will still have to be much larger than the piece of candy, since there are very few grams in a given volume of Nerf ball material.

12. The density would still be 60.0 g/cm^3. Density refers to the amount of mass that is contained in a given volume of something (like 1 cm^3). The mass of an object is the same on the Moon as it is on Earth. The weight of the object, on the other hand, would only be $\frac{1}{6}$ of what it is on Earth. The density of an object does not depend on its weight, only on its mass.

13. $\frac{1 \text{ cm}^3}{5.4 \times 10^9 \text{ blood cells}}$ = 1.9 × 10^{-10} cm^3/blood cell

    Note: The density of the blood cells was irrelevant. If you want to know the number of cubic centimeters occupied by 1 blood cell, just divide the total volume of all the blood cells by the number of blood cells that you have.

Lecture Five
The SI (Metric) System of Measurement

1. Meters, length, m

   Kilograms, mass, kg

   Seconds, time, s

   Kelvin, temperature, K

   Moles, amount of a substance, mol

2. **A.** Kilograms, grams
   B. Cubic meters, cubic centimeters/milliliters/liters
   C. Kelvin, degrees Celsius
   D. Meters per second, kilometers per hour

3. Giga, 10^9; Mega, 10^6; Kilo, 10^3

4. Centi, 10^{-2}; milli, 10^{-3}; micro, 10^{-6}; nano, 10^{-9}

5. There are 2 main goals in defining any metric unit: (1) It must be defined in terms of something that is assumed will remain the same for all time and cannot be lost, stolen, or destroyed. (2) It must be defined in terms of something that can be measured with great accuracy. The definition of the meter has undergone several revisions to accomplish these goals.

6. The kilogram

7. **A.** A 2-kilo mockingbird
   B. Tera-bull
   C. A mega-phone
   D. A micro-phone
   E. An atto-boy
   F. A deca-cards
   G. A micro-fish (microfiche)
   H. A deca-ration
   I. A centi-pede
   J. Deca-dent

Lecture Six
Converting between Systems of Measurement

1. 3.77 mm $= 0.377$ cm (from 10^{-3} to 10^{-2})

2. 9.18 mm $= 9.18 \times 10^3$ μm (from 10^{-3} to 10^{-6})

3. 7.93 Gmol $= 7.93 \times 10^{18}$ nmol (from 10^9 to 10^{-9})

4. 5.85×10^{-7} Mg $= 5.85 \times 10^8$ ng (from 10^6 to 10^{-9}—15 powers of 10, and $10^{-7} \times 10^{15} = 10^8$)

5. 7.22×10^6 dg $= 7.22 \times 10^2$ kg (from 10^{-1} to 10^3—4 powers of 10, and $10^6 \times 10^{-4} = 10^2$)

6. 1.81 Ym $= 1.81 \times 10^{36}$ pm (from 10^{24} to 10^{-12})

7. $(167 \text{ cm})(\frac{1 \text{ in}}{2.54 \text{ cm}}) = 65.7$ in

8. $(1.33 \text{ lb})(453.6 \text{ g/lb})(\frac{1 \text{ kg}}{1000 \text{ g}}) = 0.603$ kg

9. $(1 \text{ cm})(\frac{1 \text{ in}}{2.54 \text{ cm}})(\frac{1 \text{ ft}}{12 \text{ in}})(\frac{1 \text{ mi}}{5280 \text{ ft}}) = 6.21 \times 10^{-6}$ cm

10. $(1{,}000{,}000 \text{ s})(\frac{1 \text{ min}}{60 \text{ s}})(\frac{1 \text{ h}}{60 \text{ min}})(\frac{1 \text{ day}}{24 \text{ h}}) = 11.6$ days

11. $\frac{6.5 \times 10^5 \text{ lb}}{1.0 \times 10^5 \text{ gal}} = 6.5$ lb/gal

    $(6.5 \text{ lb/gal})(453.6 \text{ g/lb})(\frac{1 \text{ gal}}{4 \text{ qt}})(1.06 \text{ qt/L})(\frac{1 \text{ L}}{1000 \text{ mL}})(\frac{1 \text{ mL}}{1 \text{ cm}^3}) =$

    0.78 g/cm^3

12. First, you need to compute the volume of the necklace:

    $(18 \text{ in})(2.54 \text{ cm/in}) = 45.72$ cm

    1.0 mm $= 0.10$ cm

    $(45.72 \text{ cm})(1.0 \text{ cm})(0.10 \text{ cm}) = 4.572$ cm^3

    Then, using the density of gold, calculate the mass:

    $(4.572 \text{ cm}^3)(19.0 \text{ g/cm}^3) = 86.9$ g

13. $\frac{100 \text{ mi}}{1.75 \times 10^5 \text{ mi/h}} = 5.71 \times 10^{-4}$ h

    $(5.71 \times 10^{-4} \text{ h})(60 \text{ min/h})(60 \text{ s/min}) = 2.1$ s

14. $\frac{1 \text{ cm}}{3.0 \times 10^{10} \text{ cm/s}} = 3.33 \times 10^{-11}$ s $= 3.33 \times 10^{-2}$ ns

15. $(3.0 \times 10^{10} \text{ cm/s})(60 \text{ s/min})(60 \text{ min/h})(24 \text{ h/day})(365 \text{ days/year}) = 9.46 \times 10^{17}$ cm/year

    $(9.46 \times 10^{17} \text{ cm})(\frac{1 \text{ in}}{2.54 \text{ cm}})(\frac{1 \text{ ft}}{12 \text{ in}})(\frac{1 \text{ mi}}{5280 \text{ ft}}) = 5.88 \times 10^{12}$ mi

    This is almost 6 trillion miles!

16. 1 blintz = 1 ngogn of halavah

1 ngogn = 1000 p^3

1 p^3 = (2.26335 mm)^3 = 11.59458351 mm^3

1 ngogn = (1000)(11.59458351 mm^3) = 11,594.58351 mm^3

1 ngogn = (11,594.58351 mm^3)$(\frac{1\ cm}{10\ mm})^3$ = 11.59458351 cm^3

Mass of 1 ngogn of halavah = (11.59458351 cm^3)(3.1416 g/cm^3) = 36.43 g

Mass of 1 blintz = 36.43 g

Lecture Seven
Elements, Atoms, and the Periodic Table

1. An operational definition is a definition expressed in terms of operations or tests that can be performed to see if something fits into that category or set of things that you are trying to define. If it passes the test, it is included.

    An operational definition of a circle might simply be that it is a smooth line with no breaks or corners that bends around and rejoins itself, like a snake biting its own tail, and it looks the same no matter how you rotate it or from which direction you look at it. (Note: This is certainly not the best definition, but it is these kinds of properties that allow little children to identify circles long before they understand what they actually are or can verbally explain how they know which shapes are circles and which are not. I hope trying to come up with this definition has shown you how difficult it can often be to define something clearly and unambiguously. There are almost always things that do not quite fit, whatever definition we might come up with.)

2. A conceptual definition is a definition expressed in terms that allow us to understand why something belongs to that set of things established by the definition. The conceptual definition of a circle might be that it is a curved line around a center point, where every point on the line is equidistant from the center point.

3. Operational: An element is a substance that cannot be broken down into simpler substances by ordinary physical or chemical techniques.

    Conceptual: A substance that contains only one kind of atom.

4. He predicted the existence of several undiscovered elements that later were discovered.

5. H, He, Li, C, N, O, F, Ne, Na, Mg, Al, Si, P, S, Cl, Ar, K, Ca, Cr, Fe, Ni, Cu, Zn, Br, Ag, Sn, I, Xe, Ba, Au, Hg, Pb, Bi, Rn, and U.

6. The atomic number tells us how many protons are in the nucleus of that atom and/or the number of electrons in the atom.

7. The charge +1, where the 1 simply represents 1 elementary charge.

8. The charge is −1, where the 1 simply represents 1 elementary charge.

9. In the operational definition, we need to further understand what is meant by "ordinary physical and chemical techniques." In the conceptual definition, does "one kind of atom" mean that an element cannot contain different isotopes of the same atom? (It does not—all isotopes are considered to be the same kind of atom when defining an element, but that is not apparent from the definition as given.)

10. If we could charge 3 different spheres and then found that any combination of 2 would attract each other, then we would have to conclude that there were 3 different kinds of charges instead of only 2. In reality, it is impossible to charge 3 spheres without at least 1 combination repelling each other, which indicates that there are only 2 different kinds of charges.

11. **A.** Ba

    B. Ag

    C. He

    D. Si

    E. Te

    F. Zn

    G. B

Lecture Eight
Ions, Compounds, and Interpreting Formulas

1. D

2. F; both A and B are correct.

3. Protons exist inside the nucleus of an atom. To alter an atom's nucleus requires far more energy than would ever be involved in a chemical process.

4. **A.** OH^-

    B. NO_3^-

    C. SO_4^{2-}

    D. CO_3^{2-}

    E. $C_2H_3O_2^-$

    F. $Cr_2O_4^{2-}$

    G. $Cr_2O_7^{2-}$

5. **A.** 1 sulfur, 3 oxygen, 2 extra electrons

    B. 1 phosphorus, 4 oxygen, 3 extra electrons

    C. 1 nitrogen, 4 hydrogen, 1 missing electron

    D. 3 hydrogen, 1 phosphorus, 4 oxygen, 1 extra electron

    E. 2 sulfur, 3 oxygen, 2 extra electrons

    F. 1 iron, 6 carbon, 6 nitrogen, 4 extra electrons

6. **A.** FeN

    B. Cr_2S_3

    C. $Ba(CN)_2$

    D. KNO_3

    E. $Al_2(Cr_2O_7)_3$

    F. $Sn(SO_4)_2$

    G. $Sn_3(PO_4)_4$

7. **A.** 1 aluminum, 6 carbon, 9 hydrogen, 6 oxygen

    B. 2 chromium, 6 sulfur, 9 oxygen

    C. 1 iron, 6 hydrogen, 3 phosphorus, 12 oxygen

    D. 2 nitrogen, 8 hydrogen, 2 chromium, 7 oxygen

8. **A.** 1 iron, 1 nitrogen

    B. 2 chromium, 3 sulfur

    C. 1 barium, 2 carbon, 2 nitrogen

    D. 1 potassium, 1 nitrogen, 3 oxygen

E. 2 aluminum, 6 chromium, 21 oxygen

F. 1 tin, 2 sulfur, 8 oxygen

H. 3 tin, 4 phosphorus, 16 oxygen

9. CO is carbon monoxide, and it consists of individual, separated CO molecules, each consisting of 1 atom of carbon and 1 atom of oxygen. NaCl consists of an enormous aggregate of sodium and chloride ions. There are no individual NaCl molecules. You cannot say that any particular Na^+ ion is attached to any particular Cl^- ion. Consequently, we say that NaCl simply represents the formula for sodium chloride, and thus NaCl is a formula unit (i.e., 1 unit of this formula).

10. The atomic weight tells us how heavy an atom of that element is compared to the atoms of any other element.

11. All we have to do to answer this is compare the ratio of their atomic weights: Al/Fe = $\frac{27.0}{55.8}$ = 0.48. Thus an aluminum atom is a bit less than half as heavy as an iron atom, or you can say that an atom of iron is a little over twice as heavy as an aluminum atom.

12. Ba/Ag = $\frac{137.3}{107.9}$ = 1.27. Thus a barium atom is 1.27 times as heavy as a silver atom. Be sure to take the ratio of their atomic weights, not their atomic numbers.

13. Proton: charge +1, mass = 1.0073 amu (about 1 amu)

    Neutron: charge 0 (no charge), mass = 1.0087 amu (about 1 amu)

    Electron: charge −1, mass = 0.00055 amu (almost nothing)

14. **A.** 1 copper, 1 sulfur, 9 oxygen, 10 hydrogen

    B. 7 iron, 18 carbon, 18 nitrogen

Lecture Nine
Isotopes and Families of Elements

1. **A.** 27 protons, 32 neutrons, 27 electrons

   B. 79 protons, 118 neutrons, 79 electrons

   C. 24 protons, 28 neutrons, 22 electrons

   D. 7 protons, 8 neutrons, 10 electrons

   E. 93 protons, 144 neutrons, 90 electrons

2. The atomic number refers to the number of protons in the nucleus of an atom. The mass number refers to the total number of protons and neutrons in the nucleus of a particular atom. The atomic weight refers to the average weight of all the isotopes of a particular element.

3. C. Since ^{45}X is by far the most abundant isotope, the average atomic weight should come out to be just a bit below 45.

4. Metals and nonmetals. Metals are much more abundant. They are usually separated from each other by a staircase-like line near the upper-right side of the periodic table.

5. **A.** False. The properties of different metals vary, so we can hardly know the element's properties with any great degree of specificity. What we can do is make statements about what its general properties probably are, although we might be wrong in any particular case.

   B. False. We cannot even be certain of its general properties, although this is a much more reasonable statement, so if you answered true, I would not judge that to be an indefensible answer.

   C. True. We can state what its general properties probably are. Although any particular metal may not fit our generalizations, the odds are with us.

   D. False. If we know an element is a metal, we can state with some confidence that it probably forms positive ions, its clean surface is probably shiny, it probably is a good conductor of heat and electricity, and it probably is malleable and ductile (although any specific metal may lack 1 or more of these properties).

6. A. The properties listed are properties of nonmetals. Iron and sodium are metals. Helium is a noble gas.

7. **A.** No. Metals typically form positive ions.

   B. Yes. Nonmetals typically form negative ions.

   C. No. The charge on its ions does not indicate anything about how reactive it is.

   D. No. Although oxygen does form −2 ions, so do other elements, such as sulfur and selenium.

8. D and E

9. The first 2 columns and the last 6 columns

10. **A.** Halogen

    B. Alkaline earth metal

    C. Noble gas

    D. Alkali metal

    E. Chalcogen

11. **A.** Chalcogens

  B. Halogens

  C. Alkali metals

  D. Alkaline earth metals

  E. Noble gases

12. **A.** $1.0 + 2(12.0) + 3(1.0) + 2(16.0) = 60.0$ amu

  B. $137.3 + 2(14.0) + 6(16.0) = 261.3$ am

  C. $3(40.1) + 2(31.0) + 8(16.0) = 310.3$ amu

  D. $3(14.0) + 12(1.0) + 74.9 + 4(16.0) = 192.9$ amu

13. $E = mc^2$

  $m = E/c^2$

  $m = \dfrac{350 \times 10^3 \text{ J}}{(3 \times 10^8 \text{ m/s})^2}$

  Note: We will not analyze these units. Doing so requires a knowledge of joules (J) from physics, a course typically taken after chemistry in high school. Instead, we will simply attach the proper units to our final answer, which we know will have units of mass.

  $m = \dfrac{350 \times 10^3}{9 \times 10^{16}}$

  $m = 3.33 \times 10^{-12}$ kg $= 3.33 \times 10^{-9}$ g, or 0.00000000333 g, which is hardly measurable

14. This is a question that is sometimes asked by outstanding thinking students and even pops up occasionally on chemistry Listservs. How could you possibly average the numbers 16, 17, and 18 and get an average that was below 16? The answer lies in the fact that ^{16}O, for example, does not have an actual mass of 16. That is its mass number. The actual mass is a bit less than 16, because of the effect discussed in the previous question. This fact, coupled with the fact that naturally occurring oxygen is about 99.762% ^{16}O, with only small amounts of ^{17}O and ^{18}O, allows the average atomic weight to actually be a bit less than 16.

15. Average atomic weight $= (0.05 \times 42) + (0.08 \times 43) + (0.87 \times 45) = 44.69$

Lecture Ten
The Mole

1. (Yellow marble mass/blue marble mass) − ($\frac{9.71}{5.21}$) = 1.86. The mass ratio of any number of marbles would be the same, just so long as you take the same number of yellow and blue marbles.

2. It tells us that 1 mol of water, or 6.02×10^{23} molecules of water, would have a total mass of 18.0 g.

3. **A.** 12
   B. We cannot say. It depends on the car.
   C. (4 tires per car)(12 cars) = 48 tires, if we have a normal car and do not count the spare
   D. 6.02×10^{23} cars
   E. (4 tires per car)(6.02×10^{23} cars) = 24.08×10^{23} (or 2.408×10^{24}) tires

4. **A.** 6.02×10^{23} molecules
   B. (6.02×10^{23} molecules H_2O)(1 atom O per molecule) = 6.02×10^{23} atoms O
   C. (6.02×10^{23} molecules H_2O)(2 atoms H per molecule) = 1.204×10^{24} atoms H

5. They caught the same number of fish. The father caught $\frac{9.24 \text{ kg big fish}}{0.770 \text{ kg/fish}}$ = 12 fish. The son caught $\frac{2.90 \text{ kg little fish}}{0.242 \text{ kg/fish}}$ = 12 fish. The ratio of the weights of all the fish they caught ($\frac{9.24 \text{ kg}}{2.90 \text{ kg}}$ = 3.19) is about the same as the ratio of the weights of the individual fish ($\frac{0.770 \text{ kg}}{0.242 \text{ kg}}$ = 3.18), which means that they had to catch the same number of fish.

6. It illustrates the fact that if the ratio of the weights of a large number of things (like fish) is the same as the ratio of the weights of each individual thing (like 1 fish), then you have the same number of these things. Atomic and molecular weights tell us the ratio of the weights of individual atoms and molecules, in amus. Molar masses use these same numbers and just change the units from amus to grams—the ratio of the molar masses is the same as the ratio of the molecular and atomic weights. Therefore, if we weigh out a mole (1 molar mass) of anything, it will contain the same number of things as a mole of anything else.

7. **A.** 2(12.0) + 5(1.0) + 16.0 + 1.0 = 46.0 g/mol
   B. 2(12.0) + 6(1.0) + 12.0 + 1.0 + 14.0 + 2(1.0) = 59.0 g/mol
   C. 3(63.5) + 2(74.9) + 8(16.0) = 468.3 g/mol
   D. 55.8 + 3(16.0) + 3(1.0) = 106.8 g/mol
   E. 2(27.0) + 6(12.0) + 12(16.0) = 318.0 g/mol

8. F

9. B. While all of the others are meaningful quantities, it would be relatively rare to have to determine any of them when solving a problem. Grams per mole represents the number of grams it takes to have a mole of a substance—its molar mass. This is a quantity that is very often needed in order to solve a problem.

10. 63.5 + 32.1 + 4(16.0) + 5(18.0) = 249.6 g/mol (Note: I've treated the entire H_2O as a unit and used its entire molar mass of 18.0 g/mol in this calculation.)

11. There are a total of 7 atoms of Fe—4, plus an additional 3 that are inside the square brackets. There are 18 atoms of carbon—1 inside the parentheses, but taken 6 times; then these 6 are taken 3 times, for a total of 18 carbon atoms. Finally, there are 18 atoms of nitrogen, by the same reasoning.

Lecture Eleven
Solving Mole Problems

1. **A.** Less

   B. Less

   C. Less. The molar mass of water was not needed. It has nothing to do with the problem.

   D. More

   E. More. Again, the molar mass was irrelevant.

   F. Much less; 50 molecules is almost nothing. Molar mass is irrelevant.

2. **A.** Less than 1 mol

   B. $\frac{73.5 \text{ g}}{180.0 \text{ g/mol}} = 0.408$ mol

3. **A.** Less than 1 mol

   B. $\frac{8.22 \times 10^{22} \text{ molecules}}{6.02 \times 10^{23} \text{ molecules/mol}} = 0.137$ mol

4. $CH_3OH = 12.0 + 3(1.0) + 16.0 + 1.0 = 32.0$ g/mol

   $\frac{82.5 \text{ g}}{32.0 \text{ g/mol}} = 2.58$ mol

5. $(2.31 \text{ mol})(63.5 \text{ g/mol}) = 147$ g (Note: This is actually the mass, but we are using the terms mass and weight interchangeably here and will continue to do so from time to time in lecture.)

6. $\frac{2.94 \times 10^{25} \text{ molecules}}{6.02 \times 10^{23} \text{ molecules/mol}} = 48.8$ mol

7. $(23.2 \text{ mol})(6.02 \times 10^{23} \text{ molecules/mol}) = 1.40 \times 10^{25}$ molecules

8. $NaOH = 23.0 + 16.0 + 1.0 = 40.0$ g/mol

   $(0.125 \text{ mol})(40.0 \text{ g/mol}) = 5.00$ g

9. $CO_2 = 12.0 + 2(16.0) = 44.0$ g/mol

   $\frac{5.21 \text{ g}}{44.0 \text{ g/mol}} = 0.118$ mol

   $(0.118 \text{ mol})(6.02 \times 10^{23} \text{ molecules/mol}) = 7.11 \times 10^{22}$ molecules

10. $HNO_3 = 1.0 + 14.0 + 3(16.0) = 63.0$ g/mol

    $\frac{3.92 \times 10^{21} \text{ molecules}}{6.02 \times 10^{23} \text{ molecules/mol}} = 0.00651$ mol

    $(0.00651 \text{ mol})(63.0 \text{ g/mol}) = 0.410$ g HNO_3

11. $(8.50 \text{ mL})(2.91 \text{ g/mL}) = 24.735$ g Br_2

    $Br_2 = 2(79.9) = 159.8$ g/mol

    $\frac{24.735 \text{ g}}{159.8 \text{ g/mol}} = 0.1548$ mol Br_2

    $(0.1548 \text{ mol})(6.02 \times 10^{23} \text{ molecules/mol}) = 9.32 \times 10^{22}$ molecules

12. Diameter of the sphere in centimeters = (1.25 in)(2.54 cm/in) = 3.175 cm

Radius of the sphere = $\frac{3.175 \text{ cm}}{2}$ = 1.5875 cm

Volume = $\frac{4}{3}\pi r^3$ = $(\frac{4}{3})(3.1416)(1.5875 \text{ cm})^3$ = 16.758 cm^3

Mass of the sphere = (16.758 cm^3)(19.3 g/cm^3) = 323.43 g

Mass of the sphere in ounces = (323.43 g)$(\frac{1 \text{ oz}}{28.35 \text{ g}})$ = 11.408 oz

Monetary value of sphere = (11.408 oz)($850.00/oz) = $9,696.80

13. C

14. Diameter of a gold atom = 2(144 × 10^{-12} m) = 288 × 10^{-12} m

Number of gold atoms = $(\frac{1.0 \text{ g}}{196.967 \text{ g/mol}})(\frac{6.02 \times 10^{23} \text{ atoms}}{1 \text{ mol}})$ = 3.0563 × 10^{21} atoms

Length of the string of atoms = (3.0563 × 10^{21} atoms)(288 × 10^{-9} m/atom) = 8.802 × 10^{11} m

Length in miles = (8.802 × 10^{11} m)$(\frac{100 \text{ cm}}{1 \text{ m}})(\frac{1 \text{ in}}{2.54 \text{ cm}})(\frac{1 \text{ ft}}{12 \text{ in}})(\frac{1 \text{ mi}}{5280 \text{ ft}})$ = 5.47 × 10^8 mi

This is 547 million miles. If we take the distance from Earth to the Sun as about 93 million miles, this means that the atoms contained in just 1.0 g gold could stretch from here to the Sun and back almost 300 times! What this problem illustrates is that although atoms are extremely small, there are so many of them in even a small sample of material that even with their infinitesimal size, they would stretch a great distance.

Lecture Twelve
Avogadro's Hypothesis and Molar Volume

1. Molar volume refers to the volume occupied by a mole of a substance.

2. G, I, J, and H are all units that are expressed in terms of a volume per mole of material.

3. The molar volume of a substance is the volume occupied by 1 mol, or 6.02×10^{23} molecules of the substance. We would expect the amount of space taken up by this number of molecules to depend on how big the molecules are. Larger molecules should take up more space.

4. The generalization in question 3 is not true for equal volumes of gases measured at the same temperature and pressure. Equal volumes of different gases measured at the same temperature and pressure contain equal numbers of molecules. The reason this is possible is that gaseous substances at normal conditions of temperature and pressure are about 99.9% empty space. The molecules themselves only take up a very tiny fraction of the volume that the gas occupies. Since the amount of space taken up by the molecules themselves is so insignificant, it makes little difference how large or small these molecules are.

5. At the same conditions of temperature and pressure, equal volumes of different gases contain the same number of molecules. It is not exactly true, since the size of the molecules does make a small difference, but the difference is so insignificant that this hypothesis can be assumed to be true for most gases at reasonable temperatures and pressures.

6. **A.** True. A large bottle of soda is about 2 L.

   B. True

   C. True

   D. True. A basketball has a volume of a bit more than 6 L.

7. Two conditions must be met before this number can be used: (1) We must be talking about a gaseous substance; 22.414 L/mol does not apply to solids or liquids, and (2) the gas must be at STP. If it is at a different temperature and/or pressure, then 22.414 L/mol does not apply.

8. **A.** Grams per mole

   B. Liters per mole

   C. Molecules per mole

9. $\frac{7.78 \text{ L}}{22.414 \text{ L/mol}} = 0.347$ mol

10. $(6.85 \text{ mol})(22.414 \text{ L/mol}) = 154$ L

11. First find the number of moles of CO_2—you will need the molar mass.

    $\frac{11.27 \text{ g}}{44 \text{ g/mol}} = 0.256$ mol CO_2

    $(0.256 \text{ mol})(22.414 \text{ L/mol}) = 5.74$ L

12. $\frac{84.5 \text{ L}}{22.414 \text{ L/mol}} = 3.77$ mol

    $(3.77 \text{ mol})(6.02 \times 10^{23} \text{ molecules/mol}) = 2.27 \times 10^{24}$ molecules

13. Since this problem asks for grams, we will need the molar mass of SF_6.

$SF_6 = 32.1 + 6(19) = 146.1$ g/mol

$\dfrac{31.2 \text{ L}}{22.414 \text{ L/mol}} = 1.39$ mol SF_6

$(1.39 \text{ mol})(146.1 \text{ g/mol}) = 203$ g

14. $\dfrac{8.15 \times 10^{21} \text{ molecules}}{6.02 \times 10^{23} \text{ molecules/mol}} = 0.01354$ mol

$(0.01354 \text{ mol})(22.414 \text{ L/mol}) = 0.303$ L

15. $(6.22 \text{ mol})(44.0 \text{ g/mol}) = 274$ g

Note: This was a simple but trick problem. Since nothing was asked or given about the volume of the carbon dioxide gas, there was no reason to grab the 22.414 number. But students often do this reflexively when they read the phrase "gas at STP." Think before you calculate!

16. $\dfrac{9.92 \text{ g}}{44.0 \text{ g/mol}} = 0.2255$ mol CO_2

$(0.2255 \text{ mol})(6.02 \times 10^{23} \text{ molecules/mol}) = 1.36 \times 10^{23}$ molecules

Again, there's no reason to bring 22.414 L/mol into this problem, since nothing is given or asked about volume.

17. $NaCl = 23.0 + 35.5 = 58.5$ g/mol

Molar volume is the volume of 1 mol. For sodium chloride, this would be the volume occupied by 58.5 g.

$\dfrac{58.5 \text{ g}}{2.16 \text{ g/cm}^3} = 27.1 \text{ cm}^3$

This is much smaller, because the answer is in cubic centimeters, not liters. We would expect this because solids occupy much smaller volumes than gases for the same number of particles.

18. A cubic meter is 100 cm on a side, so the volume of this cube in cubic centimeters would be $(100 \text{ cm})^3$, or 10^6 cm^3. There are 1000 cm^3 in a liter (a cm^3 is the same as a mL—do not let the "centi" part of the name throw you off). Therefore, $1 \text{ m}^3 = (10^6 \text{ cm}^3)(\frac{1 \text{ L}}{1000 \text{ cm}^3}) = 1000$ L.

19. Volume of 1 Ne atom $= \frac{4}{3}\pi r^3 = (\frac{4}{3})(3.1416)(71.00 \times 10^{-12} \text{ m})^3 = 1.50 \times 10^{-30} \text{ m}^3$

$(1.50 \times 10^{-30} \text{ m}^3)(1000 \text{ L/m}^3) = 1.50 \times 10^{-27}$ L

Volume of 1 mol Ne atoms $= (1.5 \times 10^{-27} \text{ L/atom})(6.02 \times 10^{23} \text{ atoms/mol}) = 0.0009025$ L

Percentage of molar volume actually occupied by Ne atoms $= (\frac{0.0009025 \text{ L}}{22.414 \text{ L}})(100) = 0.00403\%$

Percentage of empty space $= 100 - 0.00403 = 99.996\%$

Lecture Thirteen
Percent Composition and Empirical Formulas

1. Total mass of compound = 17.204 + 7.062 + 14.080 = 38.346 g

   $\%K = \frac{17.204 \text{ g}}{38.346 \text{ g}} \times 100 = 44.87\%$

   $\%S = \frac{7.062 \text{ g}}{38.346 \text{ g}} \times 100 = 18.42\%$

   $\%O = \frac{14.080 \text{ g}}{38.346 \text{ g}} \times 100 = 36.72\%$

2. 5.68 g total compound − 1.55 g C = 4.13 g O

   $\%C = \frac{1.55 \text{ g}}{5.68 \text{ g}} \times 100 = 27.3\%$

   $\%O = \frac{4.13 \text{ g}}{5.68 \text{ g}} \times 100 = 72.7\%$

3. Assume you have 1 mol $(NH_4)_2CO_3$. It would contain the following:

   2(14.0) = 28.0 g N

   8(1.0) = 8.0 g H

   1(12.0) = 12.0 g C

   3(16.0) = 48.0 g O

   We then calculate the total molar mass of the compound.

   28.0 g + 8.0 g + 12.0 g+ 48.0 g = 96.0 g/mol

   From there, we can determine the percent composition.

   $\%N = \frac{28.0 \text{ g}}{96.0 \text{ g}} \times 100 = 29.2\%$

   $\%H = \frac{8.0 \text{ g}}{96.0 \text{ g}} \times 100 = 8.3\%$

   $\%C = \frac{12.0 \text{ g}}{96.0 \text{ g}} \times 100 = 12.5\%$

   $\%O = \frac{48.0 \text{ g}}{96.0 \text{ g}} \times 100 = 50.0\%$

4. Assume you have 1 mol $Fe_2(MnO_4)_3$. It would contain the following:

$2(55.8) = 111.6$ g Fe

$3(54.9) = 164.7$ g Mn

$12(16.0) = 192.0$ g O

Then the total molar mass:

111.6 g $+ 164.7$ g $+ 192.0$ g $= 468.3$ g/mol

And the percent composition:

$\%Fe = \frac{111.6 \text{ g}}{468.3 \text{ g}} \times 100 = 23.8\%$

$\%Mn = \frac{164.7 \text{ g}}{468.3 \text{ g}} \times 100 = 35.2\%$

$\%O = \frac{192.0 \text{ g}}{468.3 \text{ g}} \times 100 = 41.0\%$

5. Remember that the empirical formula is the simplest formula—that is, the formula with the lowest possible whole-number ratio of the atoms of the elements in the compound.
    A. CH
    B. $Na_2Cr_2O_7$
    C. $C_6H_{15}N$
    D. C_4H_5NO

6. Assume 1 mol $C_8H_{10}N_2O_2$. It would contain the following:

$8(12.0) = 96.0$ g C

$10(1.0) = 10.0$ g H

$2(14.0) = 28.0$ g N

$2(16.0) = 32.0$ g O

Then the total molar mass:

96.0 g $+ 10.0$ g $+ 28.0$ g $+ 32.0$ g $= 166.0$ g/mol

And the percent composition:

$\%C = \frac{96.0 \text{ g}}{166.0 \text{ g}} \times 100 = 57.8\%$

$\%H = \frac{10.0 \text{ g}}{166.0 \text{ g}} \times 100 = 6.0\%$

$\%N = \frac{28.0 \text{ g}}{166.0 \text{ g}} \times 100 = 16.9\%$

$\%O = \frac{32.0 \text{ g}}{166.0 \text{ g}} \times 100 = 19.3\%$

7. The answer is the same. The empirical formula must contain the same relative amounts of each element. All that happens if you do the calculation is that every number is divided by 2. The %C, for example, would just be $\frac{48.0 \text{ g}}{83.0 \text{ g}} \times 100 = 57.8\%$, and so forth.

8. You are paying $9.00/kg for the axinite and selling the aluminum for $50.00/kg, but only a small fraction of the axinite is actually aluminum. You will make a profit if you can sell the aluminum for a high enough price to compensate for all the other elements that you pay for when you buy the axinite but never would be able to sell.

Let's compute the percentage of aluminum in axinite.

The molar mass of axinite is as follows:

$1(1.0) + 3(40.1) + 2(27.0) + 10.8 + 4(28.1) + 16(16.0) = 554.5$ g/mol

We then calculate the percentage of aluminum:

$\%Al = \frac{54.0 \text{ g}}{554.5 \text{ g}} \times 100 = 9.74\%$

So for each kilogram of axinite that you process, you only obtain 0.0974 kg Al.

At $50.00/kg, you calculate the value of the aluminum:

$(0.0974 \text{ kg})(\$50.00/\text{kg}) = \$4.86$

He tried to scam you, but you were too smart for him because you know your chemistry!

Lecture Fourteen
Solving Empirical Formula Problems

1. A and B. You can calculate C and D from the formula (and a table of atomic weights), but the subscripts do not tell you directly.

2. A, C, D, and E would all have the same percent composition because they all have the same empirical formula: C_2H_3O.

3. If there are only 2 elements in the compound, then the %O would have to be $100 - 40.07$, or 59.93%.

    To determine the empirical formula, assume 100 g of the compound. From the percent composition, we know that this sample would contain 40.07 g S and 59.93 g O. We can determine how many moles there are of each element using their known molar masses.

    $$\frac{40.07 \text{ g}}{32.1 \text{ g/mol}} = 1.25 \text{ mol S}$$

    $$\frac{59.93 \text{ g}}{16.0 \text{ g/mol}} = 3.75 \text{ mol O}$$

    Bringing those 2 results together produces a formula of $S_{1.25}O_{3.75}$. Dividing both subscripts by 1.25 to find the simplest whole-number ratio gives us an empirical formula of SO_3.

4. Again, assume 100 g of the compound and determine how many moles there are of each element.

    $$\frac{13.53 \text{ g}}{55.8 \text{ g/mol}} = 0.242 \text{ mol Fe}$$

    $$\frac{39.93 \text{ g}}{54.9 \text{ g/mol}} = 0.726 \text{ mol Mn}$$

    $$\frac{46.53 \text{ g}}{16.0 \text{ g/mol}} = 2.91 \text{ mol O}$$

    Bringing those 3 results together produces a formula of $Fe_{0.242}Mn_{0.726}O_{2.91}$. Dividing all the subscripts by 0.242 produces an empirical formula of $FeMn_3O_{12}$.

5. First, the percentage of sulfur in the compound must be $100 - 57.10 - 4.76 = 38.14\%$. Assume 100 g of the compound and proceed as in the last 2 questions.

    $$\frac{57.10 \text{ g}}{12.0 \text{ g/mol}} = 4.76 \text{ mol C}$$

    $$\frac{4.76 \text{ g}}{1.0 \text{ g/mol}} = 4.76 \text{ mol H}$$

    $$\frac{38.14 \text{ g}}{32.1 \text{ g/mol}} = 1.19 \text{ mol S}$$

    This produces a formula of $C_{4.76}H_{4.76}S_{1.19}$. Dividing all the subscripts by 1.19 produces an empirical formula of C_4H_4S.

6. The percentage of oxygen in the uranium oxide must be $100 - 84.7 = 15.3\%$.

Assume 100 g of the compound and continue as before.

$$\frac{84.7\text{ g}}{238.0\text{ g/mol}} = 0.356 \text{ mol U}$$

$$\frac{15.3\text{ g}}{16.0\text{ g/mol}} = 0.956 \text{ mol O}$$

This produces a formula of $U_{0.356}O_{0.956}$. Dividing both subscripts by 0.356 produces a formula of $UO_{2.68}$. Now you have to recognize that 2.68 is about $2\frac{2}{3}$. To rid the formula of fractions, multiple both subscripts by the denominator 3. This produces an empirical formula of U_3O_8.

7. The percentage of oxygen in the compound must be $100 - 30.43 = 69.57\%$.

Assume 100 g of the compound and continue.

$$\frac{30.43\text{ g}}{14.0\text{ g/mol}} = 2.17 \text{ mol N}$$

$$\frac{69.57\text{ g}}{16.0\text{ g/mol}} = 4.35 \text{ mol O}$$

This produces a formula of $N_{2.17}O_{4.35}$. Dividing both subscripts by 2.17 produces an empirical formula of NO_2. If this were the actual molecular formula, its molar mass would be $1(14.0) + 2(16.0) = 46$ g/mol. Since the actual molar mass is 92.0 g/mol, and since $\frac{92.0}{46.0} = 2$, the molecular formula must be twice the empirical formula, or N_2O_4.

8. Assume 100 g of the compound.

$$\frac{30.19\text{ g}}{12.0\text{ g/mol}} = 2.52 \text{ mol C}$$

$$\frac{5.03\text{ g}}{1.0\text{ g/mol}} = 5.03 \text{ mol H}$$

$$\frac{44.60\text{ g}}{35.5\text{ g/mol}} = 1.26 \text{ mol Cl}$$

$$\frac{20.17\text{ g}}{32.1\text{ g/mol}} = 0.628 \text{ mol S}$$

This produces a formula of $C_{2.52}H_{5.03}Cl_{1.26}S_{0.628}$. Dividing all subscripts by 0.628 produces an empirical formula of $C_4H_8Cl_2S$. If this were the molecular formula, the molar mass of the compound would be $4(12.0) + 8(1.0) + 2(35.5) + 32.1 = 159.1$ g/mol. Since this actually is the molar mass, in this case the empirical formula does represent the actual formula.

Lecture Fifteen
Writing and Balancing Chemical Equations

1. A chemical reaction is a process where 1 or more substances are transformed into 1 or more different substances.

2. Some indications that a chemical reaction has occurred are the formation of a precipitate, the production of a gas, a color change, or a temperature change that occurs even though we did not heat or cool the system. Making these observations does not guarantee that a chemical reaction has occurred, but it is an indication. The formation of a precipitate and the production of a gas are stronger indicators than just a color change or a change in temperature. Temperature changes are particularly suspect and not all that strong an indication.

3. B and E. (B can be argued because the word "usually" is somewhat ambiguous, but this is generally true.)

4. A and B

5. B and C

6.   A. $6Mg + P_4 \rightarrow 2Mg_3P_2$

   B. $C_4H_9OH + 6O_2 \rightarrow 4CO_2 + 5H_2O$

   C. $N_2H_4 + 3O_2 \rightarrow 2NO_2 + 2H_2O$

   D. $2K + 2H_2O \rightarrow 2KOH + H_2$ (or $K + H_2O \rightarrow KOH + \frac{1}{2}H_2$)

   E. $Br_2 + 2H_2O + SO_2 \rightarrow 2HBr + H_2SO_4$

   F. $S_8 + 12O_2 \rightarrow 8SO_3$

   G. $2Na_2O_2 + 2H_2O \rightarrow 4NaOH + O_2$ (or $Na_2O_2 + H_2O \rightarrow 2NaOH + \frac{1}{2}O_2$)

   H. $3Ca(NO_3)_2 + 2FePO_4 \rightarrow Ca_3(PO_4)_2 + 2Fe(NO_3)_3$

   I. $Mg_3N_2 + 6H_2O \rightarrow 3Mg(OH)_2 + 2NH_3$

   J. $SO_2Cl_2 + 8HBr \rightarrow H_2S + 2HCl + 4Br_2 + 2H_2O$

   Note: If you need more practice, just do a Google search using the phrase "balancing chemical equations" and you will find enough equations to keep you busy for years.

7.   A. $C_{25}H_{52} + 38O_2 \rightarrow 25CO_2 + 26H_2O$ (Did you remember "HONClBrIF," our mnemonic device for remembering the diatomic elements?)

   B. $3AgNO_3 + CrCl_3 \rightarrow 3AgCl + Cr(NO_3)_3$

8.   A. $6S_2Cl_2 + 16NH_3 \rightarrow N_4S_4 + 12NH_4Cl + S_8$

   B. $4FeCr_2O_4 + 8Na_2CO_3 + 7O_2 \rightarrow 8Na_2CrO_4 + 2Fe_2O_3 + 8CO_2$

   (or $2FeCr_2O_4 + 4Na_2CO_3 + \frac{7}{2}O_2 \rightarrow 4Na_2CrO_4 + Fe_2O_3 + 4CO_2$, or even some other fraction of the whole-number coefficients)

   C. Believe it or not, there are multiple correct answers! Here are 2:

   $4XeF_4 + 8H_2O \rightarrow 2XeO_3 + 2Xe + 16HF + O_2$

   $6XeF_4 + 12H_2O \rightarrow 2XeO_3 + 4Xe + 24HF + 3O_2$

9. $10K_4Fe(CN)_6 + 122KMnO_4 + 299H_2SO_4 \rightarrow 162KHSO_4 + 5Fe_2(SO_4)_3 + 122MnSO_4 + 60HNO_3 + 60CO_2 + 188H_2O$

Lecture Sixteen
An Introduction to Stoichiometry

1. **A.** False. The coefficients tell you nothing about how many moles of reactants and products are actually in the container. You can obviously put in any amount of the reactants and products into the container that you wish.

   B. False. See above.

   C. False. Although the coefficients do not automatically tell you this, you could calculate it.

   D. True. This is the most important thing to understand.

   E. True.

   F. False. You do not have to mix reactants and products in the mole ratio given in the equation for them to react. If you mix them in a different ratio, all that happens is that one reactant will get all used up and the others will be in excess and will remain after the reaction is complete.

2. For the equation $2SO_2 + S_2Cl_2 + 3Cl_2 \rightarrow 4SOCl_2$:

   A. 2 mol SO_2 ——— 1 mol S_2Cl_2

   1 mol SO_2 ——— $\frac{1}{2}$ mol S_2Cl_2

   7.00 mol SO_2 ——— $(7.00)(\frac{1}{2}) = 3.5$ mol S_2Cl_2

   B. 3 mol Cl_2 ——— 4 mol $SOCl_2$

   1 mol Cl_2 ——— $\frac{4}{3}$ mol $SOCl_2$

   1.95 mol Cl_2 ——— $(1.95)(\frac{4}{3}) = 2.60$ mol $SOCl_2$

   C. Since this problem is asking for grams of S_2Cl_2, we will need to calculate its molar mass.

   $S_2Cl_2 = 2(32.1) + 2(35.5) = 135.2$ g/mol

   4 mol $SOCl_2$ ——— 1 mol S_2Cl_2

   1 mol $SOCl_2$ ——— $\frac{1}{4}$ mol S_2Cl_2

   9.21 mol $SOCl_2$ ——— $(9.21)(\frac{1}{4}) = 2.30$ mol S_2Cl_2

   $(2.30$ mol $S_2Cl_2)(135.2$ g/mol$) = 311$ g S_2Cl_2

   D. $Cl_2 = 2(35.5) = 71.0$ g/mol

   $\frac{5.00 \text{ g } Cl_2}{71.0 \text{ g/mol}} = 0.0704$ mol Cl_2

   3 mol Cl_2 ——— 2 mol SO_2

   1 mol Cl_2 ——— $\frac{2}{3}$ mol SO_2

   0.0740 mol Cl_2 ——— $(0.0740)(\frac{2}{3}) = 0.0469$ mol Cl_2

   E. $\frac{392.5 \text{ g } S_2Cl_2}{135.2 \text{ g/mol}} = 2.90$ mol S_2Cl_2

   1 mol S_2Cl_2 ——— 3 mol Cl_2

   2.90 mol S_cCl_2 ——— $(2.90)(3) = 8.70$ mol Cl_2

   $(8.70$ mol $Cl_2)(71.0$ g/mol$) = 618$ g Cl_2

3. $Ca_3P_2 + 6H_2O \rightarrow 2H_3P + 3Ca(OH)_2$

    A. $Ca(OH)_2 = 40.1 + 2(16.0) + 2(1.0) = 74.1$ g/mol

$$\frac{7.00 \text{ g Ca(OH)}_2}{74.1 \text{ g/mol}} = 0.0945 \text{ mol Ca(OH)}_2$$

3 mol $Ca(OH)_2$ ———— 2 mol H_3P

1 mol $Ca(OH)_2$ ———— $\frac{2}{3}$ mol H_3P

0.0945 mol $Ca(OH)_2$ ———— $(0.0945)(\frac{2}{3}) = 0.0630$ mol H_3P

    B. $Ca_3P_2 = 3(40.1) + 2(31.0) = 182.3$ g/mol

2 mol H_3P ———— 1 mol Ca_3P_2

1 mol H_3P ———— $\frac{1}{2}$ mol Ca_3P_2

6.67 mol H_3P ———— $(6.67)(\frac{1}{2}) = 3.335$ mol Ca_3P_2

$(3.335$ mol $Ca_3P_2)(182.3$ g/mol$) = 608$ g Ca_3P_2

    C. $\frac{28.39 \text{ g H}_2\text{O}}{18.0 \text{ g/mol}} = 1.577$ mol H_2O

6 mol H_2O ———— 3 mol $Ca(OH)_2$

1 mol H_2O ———— $\frac{3}{6}$ mol $Ca(OH)_2$

1.577 mol H_2O ———— $(1.577)(\frac{3}{6}) = 0.7885$ mol $Ca(OH)_2$

$(0.7885$ mol$)(74.1$ g/mol$) = 58.43$ g $Ca(OH)_2$

    D. 2 mol H_3P ———— 3 mol $Ca(OH)_2$

1 mol H_3P ———— $\frac{3}{2}$ mol $Ca(OH)_2$

4.18 mol H_3P ———— $(4.18)(\frac{3}{2}) = 6.27$ mol $Ca(OH)_2$

4. $Na_2B_4O_7 + 6CaF_2 + 7SO_3 \rightarrow 4BF_3 + 6CaSO_4 + Na_2SO_4$

    A. 7 mol SO_3 ———— 6 mol CaF_2

From this problem on, I will be representing the mole ratios as true ratios rather than doing the "x mol ———— y mol," diagram-style representation.

$(0.228$ mol $SO_3)(\frac{6 \text{ mol CaF}_2}{7 \text{ mol SO}_3}) = 0.195$ mol CaF_2

    B. $Na_2B_4O_7 = 2(23.0) + 4(10.8) + 7(16.0) = 201.2$ g/mol

$CaSO_4 = 1(40.1) + 1(32.1) + 4(16.0) = 136.2$ g/mol

$$\frac{9.00 \text{ g Na}_2\text{B}_4\text{O}_7}{201.2 \text{ g/mol}} = 0.04473 \text{ mol Na}_2\text{B}_4\text{O}_7$$

$(0.04473$ mol $Na_2B_4O_7)(\frac{6 \text{ mol CaSO}_4}{1 \text{ mol Na}_2\text{B}_4\text{O}_7}) = 0.2684$ mol $CaSO_4$

$(0.2684$ mol $CaSO_4)(136.2$ g/mol$) = 36.6$ g $CaSO_4$

    C. $BF_3 = 10.8 + 3(19.0) = 67.8$ g/mol

$$\frac{367.3 \text{ g BF}_3}{67.8 \text{ g/mol}} = 5.42 \text{ mol BF}_3$$

$(5.42$ mol $BF_3)(\frac{7 \text{ mol SO}_3}{4 \text{ mol BF}_3}) = 9.48$ mol SO_3

D. $Na_2SO_4 = 2(23) + 32.1 + 4(16) = 142.1$ g/mol

$(6.53$ mol $SO_3)(\frac{1 \text{ mol } Na_2SO_4}{7 \text{ mol } SO_3}) = 0.9329$ mol Na_2SO_4

$(0.9329$ mol $Na_2SO_4)(142.1$ g/mol$) = 133$ g Na_2SO_4

5. You decided to purchase 1 oz, or 28.35 g, of the alloy. This would cost (28.35 g)($25.00/g) = $708.75. You will make a profit if there is enough gold in that 1 oz of alloy to return more than the $708.75 you paid for the alloy in the first place. So let's calculate how many grams of gold are actually in 1 oz of the alloy.

   Since it took 34.39 g HNO_3 to completely react with all of the copper in 1 oz of the alloy, the number of grams of copper in 1 oz of the alloy can be calculated as follows:

   $HNO_3 = 1.0 + 14.0 + 3(14.0) = 63.0$ g/mol

   $\frac{34.39 \text{ g } HNO_3}{63.0 \text{ g/mol}} = 0.5459$ mol HNO_3

   $(0.5459$ mol $HNO_3)(\frac{3 \text{ mol } Cu}{8 \text{ mol } HNO_3}) = 0.2047$ mol Cu

   $(0.2047$ mol $Cu)(63.5$ g/mol$) = 13$ g Cu

   So in 1 oz, or 28.35 g, of the alloy you purchased, there were 13 g Cu, which means that there were $28.35 - 13 = 15.35$ g Au, or $\frac{15.35 \text{ g Au}}{28.35 \text{ g/oz}} = 0.5414$ oz Au. When you sell this, you would receive (0.5414 oz)($1,000.00/oz) = $541.45. It is another scam. You bought the alloy for $708.75, but only extracted enough gold to get $541.45 when you sold it.

Lecture Seventeen
Stoichiometry Problems

1. The general approach to a typical stoichiometry problem would involve the following steps:

    A. Take the amount of the starting substance and convert it into moles if it is not given in these units.

    B. Work the mole-mole problem to find the number of moles of the substance you are asked to find.

    C. Convert the moles of the substance you are asked to find into whatever units are requested.

2. A, because what you were given was given in moles, so there was no need to convert it into moles.

    D, because the coefficients represent molecule ratios as well as mole ratios.

    E, because you convert the amount of energy directly into moles of the substance requested. The energy term is treated in a manner similar to how it would be treated if it were an actual starting substance.

    F, because the coefficients represent volume ratios for gases at the same temperature and pressure.

3. For the equation $2K_2CrO_4 + 6NaCl + 16HClO_4 \rightarrow 3Cl_2(g) + 2Cr(ClO_4)_3 + 6NaClO_4 + 4KClO_4 + 8H_2O + 277$ kJ:

    A. $NaCl = 58.5$ g/mol; $KClO_4 = 138.6$ g/mol

    $\frac{8.35 \text{ g NaCl}}{58.5 \text{ g/mol}} = 0.1427$ mol NaCl

    $(0.1427 \text{ mol NaCl})(\frac{4 \text{ mol } KClO_4}{6 \text{ mol NaCl}}) = 0.09513$ mol $KClO_4$

    $(0.09513 \text{ mol } KClO_4)(138.6 \text{ g/mol}) = 13.2$ g $KClO_4$

    B. $\frac{29.91 \text{ g } KClO_4}{138.6 \text{ g/mol}} = 0.2158$ mol $KClO_4$

    $(0.2158 \text{ mol } KClO_4)(\frac{3 \text{ mol } Cl_2}{4 \text{ mol } KClO_4}) = 0.1618$ mol Cl_2

    $(0.1618 \text{ mol } Cl_2)(22.414 \text{ L/mol}) = 3.63$ L Cl_2

    C. $(3.28 \text{ mol } HClO_4)(\frac{8 \text{ mol } H_2O}{16 \text{ mol } HClO_4}) = 1.64$ mol H_2O

    $(1.64 \text{ mol } H_2O)(6.02 \times 10^{23} \text{ molecules/mol}) = 9.87 \times 10^{23}$ molecules H_2O

    D. $\frac{5.15 \text{ L } Cl_2}{22.414 \text{ L/mol}} = 0.2298$ mol Cl_2

    $(0.2298 \text{ mol } Cl_2)(\frac{277 \text{ kJ}}{3 \text{ mol } Cl_2}) = 21.2$ kJ

    E. $(733 \text{ kJ})(\frac{8 \text{ mol } H_2O}{277 \text{ kJ}}) = 21.17$ mol H_2O

    $(21.17 \text{ mol } H_2O)(6.02 \times 10^{23} \text{ molecules/mol}) = 1.27 \times 10^{25}$ molecules H_2O

    F. $HClO_4 = 100.5$ g/mol

    $(7.22 \text{ mol NaCl})(\frac{16 \text{ mol } HClO_4}{6 \text{ mol NaCl}}) = 19.25$ mol $HClO_4$

    $(19.25 \text{ mol } HClO_4)(100.5 \text{ g/mol}) = 1935$ g $HClO_4$

    G. $(4.28 \times 10^{25} \text{ molecules } H_2O)(\frac{3 \text{ molecules } Cl_2}{8 \text{ molecules } H_2O}) = 1.60 \times 10^{25}$ molecules Cl_2

    H. $(3.00 \text{ mol NaCl})(\frac{16 \text{ mol } HClO_4}{6 \text{ mol NaCl}}) = 8.00$ mol $HClO_4$

4. A. $C_6H_5NO_2 = 123.0$ g/mol

$$\frac{28.5 \text{ g } C_6H_5NO_2}{123.0 \text{ g/mol}} = 0.2317 \text{ mol } C_6H_5NO_2$$

$$(0.2317 \text{ mol } C_6H_5NO_2)(\frac{29 \text{ mol } O_2}{4 \text{ mol } C_6H_5NO_2}) = 1.68 \text{ mol } O_2$$

$$(1.68 \text{ mol } O_2)(22.414 \text{ L/mol}) = 37.7 \text{ L } O_2$$

B. $(7.33 \text{ L } O_2)(\frac{4 \text{ L } NO_2}{29 \text{ L } O_2}) = 1.01 \text{ L } NO_2$

5. $(7.37 \text{ mol B})(\frac{d \text{ mol D}}{b \text{ mol B}}) = \frac{7.37d}{b} \text{ mol D}$

$(\frac{7.37d}{b} \text{ mol D})(22.414 \text{ L/mol}) = \frac{165d}{b} \text{ L D}$

6. Using the equation $2K_2CrO_4 + 6NaCl + 16HClO_4 \rightarrow 3Cl_2(g) + 2Cr(ClO_4)_3 + 6NaClO_4 + 4KClO_4 + 8H_2O + 277$ kJ, let $x =$ grams of K_2CrO_4 in the original mixture. Then grams of NaCl in the original mixture would equal $15.00 - x$.

Set up an equation for the total number of liters of Cl_2 produced when both of these substances react, which the problem states is equal to 2.70 L.

Total liters of Cl_2 produced = (L Cl_2 produced from K_2CrO_4) + (L Cl_2 produced from NaCl)

Total liters $Cl_2 = [(\frac{x \text{ g } K_2CrO_4}{194.2 \text{ g/mol}})(\frac{3 \text{ mol } Cl_2}{2 \text{ mol } K_2CrO_4}) + (\frac{15.00 - x \text{ g NaCl}}{58.5 \text{ g/mol}})(\frac{3 \text{ mol } Cl_2}{6 \text{ mol NaCl}})](22.414 \text{ L/mol}) = 2.70$

Carrying several extra digits during the calculation, we get $(0.007723996x + 0.128205128 - 0.008547009x)(22.414) = 2.70$

$(0.128205128 - 0.000823013x)(22.414) = 2.70$

$2.8736 - 0.01845x = 2.70$

$0.01845x = 0.1736$

$x = 9.41$ g K_2CrO_4

grams of NaCl $= 15.00 - 9.41 = 5.59$ g

$\%K_2CrO_4 = \frac{9.41 \text{ g } K_2CrO_4}{15.00 \text{ g}} \times 100 = 62.7\%$

$\%NaCl = \frac{5.59 \text{ g NaCl}}{15.00 \text{ g}} \times 100 = 37.3\%$

Lecture Eighteen
Advanced Stoichiometry

1. The limiting reactant is the reactant in a chemical reaction that will limit the amount of product that can be produced. If the reactants are not mixed in the proper mole ratio, you will use up one of the reactants, while the other reactants will be in excess, with some of them being left over when the reaction stops because the limiting reactant has been consumed.

2. Given $IF_5 + 3H_2O \rightarrow HIO_3 + 5HF$:

   A. $IF_5 = 221.9$ g/mol

   $\frac{7.00 \text{ g } IF_5}{221.9 \text{ g/mol}} = 0.03155$ mol IF_5

   $\frac{0.03155 \text{ mol } IF_5}{1 \text{ mol } IF_5 \text{ /reaction}} = 0.03155$ (i.e., I have enough IF_5 to run the reaction 0.03155 times.)

   $\frac{2.00 \text{ g } H_2O}{18.0 \text{ g/mol}} = 0.1111$ mol H_2O

   $\frac{0.1111 \text{ mol } H_2O}{3 \text{ mol } H_2O \text{/reaction}} = 0.03704$ (i.e., I have enough H_2O to run the reaction 0.03704 times.)

   Since I can run the reaction fewer times with the IF_5, it is the limiting reactant.

   B. Since the molar ratio between IF_5 and HIO_3 is 1:1, I can produce 0.03155 mol HIO_3.

   $HIO_3 = 175.9$ g/mol

   (0.03155 mol HIO_3)(175.9 g/mol) = 5.54 g HIO_3

3. Given $4P_4 + 5S_8 \rightarrow 8P_2S_5$:

   A. $P_4 = 124.0$ g/mol; $S_8 = 256.8$ g/mol

   $\frac{25.00 \text{ g } P_4}{124.0 \text{ g/mol}} = 0.2016$ mol P_4

   $\frac{0.2016 \text{ mol } P_4}{4 \text{ mol } P_4 \text{ /reaction}} = 0.0504$ (i.e., I have enough P_4 to run the reaction 0.0504 times.)

   $\frac{80.00 \text{ g } S_8}{256.8 \text{ g/mol}} = 0.3115$ mol S_8

   $\frac{0.3115 \text{ mol } S_8}{5 \text{ mol } S_8 \text{ /reaction}} = 0.06231$ (i.e., I have enough S_8 to run the reaction 0.06231 times.)

   P_4 is the limiting reactant.

   B. $P_2S_5 = 222.5$ g/mol

   (0.2016 mol P_4)($\frac{8 \text{ mol } P_2S_5}{4 \text{ mol } P_4}$) = 0.4032 mol P_2S_5

   (0.4032 mol P_2S_5)(222.5 g/mol) = 89.7 g P_2S_5

   C. Calculate the number of grams of S_8 that are consumed.

   (0.2016 mol P_4)($\frac{5 \text{ mol } S_8}{4 \text{ mol } P_4}$) = 0.252 mol S_8

   (0.252 mol S_8)(256.8 g/mol) = 64.71 g S_8 consumed

   80.00 g − 64.71 g = 15.29 g S_8 in excess

4. Given $3Cl_2O(g) + 10H_3N \rightarrow 6NH_4Cl + 2N_2(g) + 3H_2O$:

   A. $H_3N = 17.0$ g/mol; $NH_4Cl = 53.5$ g/mol

   $\dfrac{9.22 \text{ mol } Cl_2O}{3 \text{ mol } Cl_2O/\text{reaction}} = 3.0733$

   $\dfrac{500.0 \text{ g } H_3N}{17.0 \text{ g/mol}} = 29.411$ mol H_3N

   $\dfrac{29.411 \text{ mol } H_3N}{10 \text{ mol } H_3N/\text{reaction}} = 2.9411$

   H_3N is the limiting reactant.

   $(29.411 \text{ mol } H_3N)(\frac{6 \text{ mol } NH_4Cl}{10 \text{ mol } H_3N}) = 17.647$ mol NH_4Cl

   $(17.647 \text{ mol } NH_4Cl)(53.5 \text{ g/mol}) = 944$ g NH_4Cl

   B. $(29.411 \text{ mol } H_3N)(\frac{2 \text{ mol } N_2}{10 \text{ mol } H_3N}) = 5.882$ mol N_2

   $(5.882 \text{ mol } N_2)(22.414 \text{ L/mol}) = 132$ L N_2

   C. Calculate the number of grams of Cl_2O consumed

   $Cl_2O = 87.0$ g/mol

   $(29.411 \text{ mol } H_3N)(\frac{3 \text{ mol } Cl_2O}{10 \text{ mol } H_3N}) = 8.823$ mol Cl_2O

   $(8.823 \text{ mol } Cl_2O)(87.0 \text{ g/mol}) = 767$ g Cl_2O consumed

   Initial Cl_2O present $= (9.22 \text{ mol } Cl_2O)(87.0 \text{ g/mol}) = 802$ g

   $802 - 767 = 35$ g Cl_2O remaining

5. Given $3Cl_2O(g) + 10H_3N \rightarrow 6NH_4Cl + 2N_2(g) + 3H_2O$:

   A. $\dfrac{81.3 \text{ L } Cl_2O}{22.414 \text{ L/mol}} = 3.627$ mol Cl_2O

   $\dfrac{3.627 \text{ mol } Cl_2O}{3 \text{ mol } Cl_2O/\text{reaction}} = 1.209$

   $\dfrac{155.0 \text{ g } H_3N}{17.0 \text{ g/mol}} = 9.118$ mol H_3N

   $\dfrac{9.118 \text{ mol } H_3N}{10 \text{ mol } H_3N/\text{reaction}} = 0.9118$

   H_3N is the limiting reactant

   $(9.118 \text{ mol } H_3N)(\frac{2 \text{ mol } N_2}{10 \text{ mol } H_3N}) = 1.8236$ mol N_2

   $(1.8236 \text{ mol } N_2)(28.0 \text{ g/mol}) = 51.1$ g N_2

   B. Calculate the number of grams of Cl_2O consumed

   $(9.118 \text{ mol } H_3N)(\frac{3 \text{ mol } Cl_2O}{10 \text{ mol } H_3N}) = 2.7354$ mol Cl_2O

   $(2.7354 \text{ mol } Cl_2O)(87.0 \text{ g/mol}) = 238$ g Cl_2O consumed

   Initial Cl_2O present $= \dfrac{81.3 \text{ L } Cl_2O}{22.414 \text{ L/mol}} = 3.6272$ mol Cl_2O

   $(3.6272 \text{ mol } Cl_2O)(87.0 \text{ g/mol}) = 316$ g Cl_2O

   $316 - 238 = 78$ g Cl_2O remaining

   C. From A, we know that the theoretical yield of N_2 is 51.1 g.

   % yield $= \dfrac{50.0 \text{ g}}{51.1 \text{ g}} \times 100 = 97.8\%$ yield

6. Given $2Sc_2O_3 + 9Cl_2(g) + 3S_2Cl_2 \rightarrow 4ScCl_3 + 6SOCl_2(g)$:

A. First let's check their calculation.

Sc$_2$O$_3$ = 138.0 g/mol; ScCl$_3$ = 151.5 g/mol

$\frac{100.0 \text{ g Sc}_2\text{O}_3}{138.0 \text{ g/mol}} = 0.7246$ mol Sc$_2$O$_3$

$(0.7246 \text{ mol Sc}_2\text{O}_3)(\frac{4 \text{ mol ScCl}_3}{2 \text{ mol Sc}_2\text{O}_3}) = 1.449$ mol ScCl$_3$

$(1.449 \text{ mol ScCl}_3)(151.3 \text{ g/mol}) = 219.2$ g ScCl$_3$

The calculation they showed was correct.

B. It is not a good deal, because Sc$_2$O$_3$ is the excess reactant, not the limiting reactant. To determine how much ScCl$_3$ we can actually produce, we will first have to determine which of the 3 reactants is actually the limiting reactant.

$\frac{0.7246 \text{ mol Sc}_2\text{O}_3}{2 \text{ mol Sc}_3\text{O}_3/\text{reaction}} = 0.3623$

$\frac{100.0 \text{ g Cl}_2}{71.0 \text{ g/mol}} = 1.408$ mol Cl$_2$

$\frac{1.408 \text{ mol Cl}_2}{9 \text{ mol Cl}_2/\text{reaction}} = 0.1564$

$\frac{100.0 \text{ g S}_2\text{Cl}_2}{135.2 \text{ g/mol}} = 0.7396$ mol S$_2$Cl$_2$

$\frac{0.7396 \text{ mol Sc}_2\text{Cl}_2}{3 \text{ mol Sc}_2\text{Cl}_2/\text{reaction}} = 0.2465$

Cl$_2$ is the limiting reactant.

Now calculate how many grams of ScCl$_3$ can be produced from the limiting reactant.

$(1.408 \text{ mol Cl}_2)(\frac{4 \text{ mol ScCl}_3}{9 \text{ mol Cl}_2}) = 0.6258$ mol ScCl$_3$

$(0.6258 \text{ mol ScCl}_3)(151.5 \text{ g/mol}) = 94.81$ g ScCl$_3$

We can sell the ScCl$_3$ for (94.81 g)($15.00/g) = $1,422.15

We would have been scammed again, except that we knew how to work limiting reactant problems!

Lecture Nineteen
An Introduction to Molarity

1. While most of these are not actually used, all the listed ratios are valid (but perhaps not very useful) ways of expressing the concentration of a solution because they are all ratios of an amount of solute (expressed in various units) to either an amount of solvent or an amount of solution.

2. B, C, D, and F. G is not correct because you need a total of 1 L solution, which would not require 1 L water.

3. The 250 mL is $\frac{1}{4}$ L. Since a 1.00 M solution contains 1 mol NaOH per liter, $\frac{1}{4}$ L of this solution would only require $\frac{1}{4}$ mol NaOH, or 10.0 g NaOH. To prepare this solution, you would get a 250-mL volumetric flask. You would add some distilled water to the flask, then add your 10.0 g of NaOH. You would swirl the flask until the NaOH dissolved completely, then add water until the total volume of the solution reaches the etch mark on the neck of the flask, which means you have a total volume of solution equal to 250 mL.

4. Neither. The first solution has a concentration of 8 drops/2.00 L, or 4. The second solution has a concentration of 1 drop/0.250 L, or 4. Since the 2 solutions have the same concentration, they should appear equally dark.

Lecture Twenty
Solving Molarity Problems

1. $\frac{0.423\ mol}{0.25\ L} = 1.69\ M$

2. $Na_2WO_4 = 2(23.0) + 183.8 + 4(16.0) = 293.8\ g/mol$

   $\frac{255\ g}{293.8\ g/mol} = 0.8679\ mol$

   $\frac{0.8679\ mol}{0.388\ L} = 2.24\ M$

3. The solution we are asked to prepare would contain the following:

   $(1.25\ mol\ K_2CrO_4/L)(0.500\ L) = 0.625\ mol\ K_2CrO_4$

   Since we have to obtain this amount of K_2CrO_4 by weighing it out, we will have to determine how much this weighs.

   $K_2CrO_4 = 2(39.1) + 52.0 + 4(16.0) = 194.2\ g/mol$

   $(0.625\ mol)(194.2\ g/mol) = 121.4\ g\ K_2CrO_4$

   You would take a 500 mL volumetric flask, pour some water into it, add the 121.4 grams of K_2CrO_4, swirl it until it dissolves, and then add enough water to reach the 500 mL etch mark on the neck of the volumetric flask.

4. $(0.333\ mol/L)(0.125\ L) = 0.0416\ mol\ HNO_3$

5. $(2.22\ mol/L)(0.038\ L) = 0.08436\ mol\ H_2SO_4$

   $(0.08436\ mol\ H_2SO_4)(98.1\ g/mol) = 8.28\ g\ H_2SO_4$

6. First, let's work this the "long" way.

   $mol\ HNO_3$ in 250 mL of 0.75 M $HNO_3 = (0.75\ mol/L)(0.250\ L) = 0.1875\ mol$

   $\frac{0.1875\ mol}{0.25\ mol/L} = 0.75\ L = 750\ mL$

   Or you can just think about it this way: Since the first solution is only $\frac{1}{3}$ as concentrated as the second, it will take 3 times the volume to obtain the same number of moles of solute.

7. $\frac{3.44\ mol}{6.00\ mol/L} = 0.573\ L = 573\ mL$

8. $C_{12}H_{22}O_{11} = 342.0\ g/mol$

   $\frac{50.00\ g}{342.0\ g/mol} = 0.1462\ mol$

   $\frac{0.1462\ mol}{3.00\ mol/L} = 0.0487\ L = 48.7\ mL$

9. Total mass of solution $= \frac{1.15\ g/mol}{1000\ mL} = 1150\ g$

   Mass of water = 922 g (since water has a density of 1.00 g/mL and you had 922 mL of H_2O)

   $1150\ g - 922\ g = 228\ g\ C_{12}H_{22}O_{11}$

   $mol\ C_{12}H_{22}O_{11} = \frac{228\ g}{342.0\ g/mol} = 0.667\ mol = 0.667\ M$ (since we prepared 1.00 L of solution)

Lecture Twenty-One
Advanced Molarity Problems

1. Here is the "grind out the answer" approach:

    mol HCl = (6.0 mol/L)(0.050 L) = 0.30 mol HCl

    $\frac{0.30 \text{ mol}}{0.100 \text{ L}} = 3.00 \text{ M}$

    Now compare the insightful approach:

    Since we are doubling the volume of the solution from 50 mL to 100 mL without adding any additional HCl, the new concentration will just have to be half the original concentration.

2. mol NaOH required = (1.00 mol/L)(0.500 L) = 0.500 mol NaOH

    $\frac{0.500 \text{ mol}}{3.25 \text{ mol/L}} = 0.154 \text{ L} = 154 \text{ mL}$

3. **A.** mol $HC_2H_3O_2$ required = (0.50 mol/L)(0.500 L) = 0.250 mol $H_2C_3O_2$

    $\frac{0.250 \text{ mol}}{17.4 \text{ mol/L}} = 0.0144 \text{ L} = 14.4 \text{ mL}$

    B. You would take a 500-mL volumetric flask, pour 14.4 mL of the glacial acetic acid into the flask, and then add water until the volume of the entire solution reached the 500 mL etch mark on the neck of the flask.

4. mol HCl coming from the first solution = (1.88 mol/L)(0.125 L) = 0.235 mol HCl

    mol HCl coming from the second solution = (0.63 mol/L)(0.722 L) = 0.455 mol HCl

    Total mol HCl in final solution = 0.235 + 0.455 = 0.690 mol HCl

    Total volume = 125 mL + 722 mL = 847 mL = 0.847 L

    $[\text{HCl}] = \frac{0.690 \text{ mol}}{0.847 \text{ L}} = 0.815 \text{ M}$

5. AgCl = 143.5 g/mol

    $\frac{9.00 \text{ g AgCl}}{143.5 \text{ g/mol}} = 0.06272 \text{ mol AgCl}$

    Since all coefficients are 1, we also have 0.06272 mol $AgNO_3$ in this reaction, and therefore:

    $\frac{0.06276 \text{ mol AgNO}_3}{1.35 \text{ mol/L}} = 0.0465 \text{ L} = 46.5 \text{ mL AgNO}_3$

6. $FeS(s) + 2HI(aq) \rightarrow H_2S(g) + FeI_2(aq)$

    mol H_2S = $\frac{6.4 \text{ L}}{22.414 \text{ L/mol}} = 0.2855 \text{ mol H}_2\text{S}$

    mol HI required = $(0.2855 \text{ mol H}_2\text{S})(\frac{2 \text{ mol HI}}{1 \text{ mol H}_2\text{S}}) = 0.571 \text{ mol HI}$

    $\frac{0.571 \text{ mol HI}}{5.00 \text{ mol/L}} = 0.114 \text{ L} = 114 \text{ mL}$

7. $Na_3PO_4 \rightarrow 3Na^+ + PO_4^{3-}$

    $[\text{Na}^+] = 3(0.42 \text{ M}) = 1.26 \text{ M}$

    $[PO_4^{3-}] = 0.42 \text{ M}$

8. A. $NaCl \rightarrow Na^+ + Cl^-$

$Na^+ = 0.18$ M

$Cl^- = 0.18$ M

B. $NaNO_3 \rightarrow Na^+ + NO_3^-$

$[Na^+] = 1.93$ M

$[NO_3^-] = 1.93$ M

C. $K_2SO_3 \rightarrow 2K^+ + SO_3^{2-}$

$[K^+] = 2(4.82 \text{ M}) = 9.64$ M

$[SO_3^{2-}] = 4.82$ M

D. $Al_2(SO_4)_2 \rightarrow 2Al^{3+} + 3SO_4^{2-}$

$[Al^{3+}] = 2(0.87 \text{ M}) = 1.74$ M

$[SO_4^{2-}] = 3(0.87 \text{ M}) = 2.61$ M

9. $Fe_2(SO_4)_3 = 399.9$ g/mol

$\frac{6.12 \text{ g}}{399.9 \text{ g/mol}} = 0.0153$ mol $Fe_2(SO_4)_3$

$\frac{0.0153 \text{ mol}}{0.085 \text{ L}} = 0.180$ M $Fe_2(SO_4)_3$

$Fe_2(SO_4)_3 \rightarrow 2Fe^{3+} + 3SO_4^{2-}$

$[Fe^{3+}] = 2(0.18 \text{ M}) = 0.36$ M

$[SO_4^{2-}] = 3(0.18 \text{ M}) = 0.54$ M

10. $3SnCl_4(aq) + 4K_3PO_4(aq) \rightarrow 12KCl(aq) + Sn_3(PO_4)_4(s)$

A. mol $SnCl_4$ = (1.85 mol/L)(0.225 L) = 0.4162 mol $SnCl_4$

$\frac{0.4162 \text{ mol SnCl}_4}{3 \text{ mol SnCl}_4/\text{reaction}} = 0.1387$

I have enough $SnCl_4$ to run the reaction 0.1387 times.

mol K_3PO_4 = (1.77 mol/L)(0.350 L) = 0.6195 mol K_3PO_4

$\frac{0.6195 \text{ mol K}_3PO_4}{4 \text{ mol K}_3PO_4/\text{reaction}} = 0.1549$

I have enough K_3PO_4 to run the reaction 0.1549 times.

Therefore, $SnCl_4$ is the limiting reactant.

B. $Sn_3(PO_4)_4 = 3(118.7) + 4(31.0) + 16(16.0) = 736.1$ g/mol

mol $Sn_3(PO_4)_4$ = (0.4162 mol $SnCl_4$)($\frac{1 \text{ mol Sn}_3(PO_4)_4}{3 \text{ mol SnCl}_4}$) = 0.1387 mol $Sn_3(PO_4)_4$

(0.1387 mol)(736.1 g/mol) = 102.1 g $Sn_3(PO_4)_4$

11. The substance in excess is K_3PO_4. First calculate how many moles of K_3PO_4 will remain when the reaction is complete:

mol K_3PO_4 consumed = (0.4162 mol $SnCl_4$)($\frac{4 \text{ mol } K_3PO_4}{3 \text{ mol } SnCl_4}$) = 0.5549 mol K_3PO_4

mol K_3PO_4 remaining = 0.6195 mol − 0.5549 mol = 0.0646 mol K_3PO_4

Total volume of solution = 225 mL + 350 mL = 575 mL = 0.575 L

$[K_3PO_4] = \frac{0.0646 \text{ mol}}{0.575 \text{ L}} = 0.112$ M

$K_3PO_4 \rightarrow 3K^+ + PO_4^{3-}$

$[K^+] = 3(0.112$ M$) = 0.336$ M

$[PO_4^{3-}] = 0.112$ M

Lecture Twenty-Two
Basic Concepts of Chemical Equilibrium

1. This means that for all practical purposes, the reaction only runs in 1 direction. The reactants just keep reacting until at least 1 of them is completely consumed.

2. A reversible reaction is basically a reaction that has at least a reasonable tendency to go in either direction—admittedly a somewhat ambiguous and nonrigorous definition, but one that hopefully helps to clarify the concept.

3. A, B, and E are true.

4. A, B, C, D, and F are true. For C, the ratio of how many moles per liter of A are consumed and of D are produced is determined by their coefficients in the balanced chemical equation. For example, suppose we started with 10 mol A and 3 mol D. If 1 mol A were consumed, then 220 mol D would be produced—period. The fact that the total number of moles of A and D in the container would end up being 9 and 5, respectively, would have nothing to do with the ratio in which they were consumed and/or produced. For D, since no C or D was initially present, they will be produced in a mole ratio the same as their coefficients in the balanced chemical equation. For F, again, the ratio at which A and B are consumed is determined by their coefficients in the balanced chemical equation.

5. The coefficients tell you the mole ratio in which the substances react with each other.

6. This is really a stoichiometry problem. It does not have anything to do with equilibrium.

    mol C = (1.50 mol D)($\frac{4 \text{ mol C}}{2 \text{ mol D}}$) = 3.00 mol C

    mol A consumed = (1.50 mol D)($\frac{3 \text{ mol A}}{2 \text{ mol D}}$) = 2.25 mol A

    mol A remaining at equilibrium = 7.00 − 2.25 = 4.75 mol A

    mol B consumed = (1.50 mol D)($\frac{1 \text{ mol B}}{2 \text{ mol C}}$) = 0.75 mol B

    mol B remaining at equilibrium = 2.00 − 0.75 = 1.25 mol B

Lecture Twenty-Three
An Introduction to the Equilibrium Constant

1. B is the only true statement. C is false because although you will produce 3 times as much C as D, you already had 1 mol C and 1 mol D to begin with. So, for example, if you were to actually produce 3 mol C and 1 mol D (an impossibility, since that would use up all of B, which is not allowed, since this is an equilibrium system, but let's keep the math simple), you would end up with a total of 4 mol C and 2 mol D at equilibrium.

2. A. $K = \frac{[H^+][F^-]}{[HF]}$

    B. $K = \frac{[NO]^2[Br_2]}{[NOBr]^2}$

    C. $K = \frac{[NH_3]^2[H_2O]}{[N_2O][H_2]^4}$

    D. $K = \frac{1}{[O_2]}$

    E. $K = [Na^+]^2[OH^-]^2[H_2]$

    F. $K = \frac{[CH_3COOH]^3[Cr^{3+}]^4}{[CH_3CH_2OH]^3[Cr_2O_7^{2-}]^2[H^+]^{16}}$

    G. $K = \frac{[N_2][NH_4Cl]^6}{[H_3N]^8[Cl_2]^3}$

3. The lines represent how the concentrations of all the reactants and products are changing with time. A straight line says that the concentrations just keep changing at a constant rate until equilibrium is achieved and then abruptly stop changing and remain constant—not too sensible, when you think about it. What actually happens is that as the rates of the forward and reverse reactions get closer and closer to being equal as you approach equilibrium, the rate at which all the concentrations are changing will become smaller and smaller. Think about that. Let's say we start with only reactants; their concentrations will be falling rather rapidly at the start, and the concentrations of the products will be rising rather rapidly. But as time passes, 2 things happen. First, as the concentration of the reactants decreases, we would expect the rate of the forward reaction to decrease. In addition, once we produce some products and the reverse reaction starts to take place, we will also be producing some reactants as well as consuming them. This means that the net rate at which the reactants are being used up will be decreasing. A similar argument applies to the rate at which the products are going to be produced. The slope of these lines will have to "flatten out," eventually becoming the horizontal lines that indicate that an equilibrium state has been achieved.

Lecture Twenty-Four
Interpreting an Equilibrium Constant

1. A silly question, since the answer is obviously zero. But students often tend, quite logically, to misspell this word as "equ*a*librium."

2. When working an equilibrium problem, you need someplace to start—something that you can write down and use as the focal point of your solution. In stoichiometry problems, we knew that the coefficients in the balanced chemical equation told us the mole ratios in which the reactants and products were related. In the case of equilibrium problems, this is often the equilibrium constant expression and the fact that, at equilibrium, its numerical value will be equal to the equilibrium constant for the reaction.

3. Because for an equilibrium constant to be negative, at least 1 of the concentrations of the reactants or products would have to have a negative concentration, which is impossible.

4. It can vary from essentially zero virtually to infinity. They are among the smallest and largest numbers you encounter in nature.

5. **A.** Probably false. A large value for K would actually tend to indicate that you would most likely have a lot more products than reactants at equilibrium. As shown in the lecture, it is possible, by using outrageously large and small concentrations, to end up with more reactants than products, but using "normal" starting concentrations you would certainly not have more reactants than products if K is large.

   B. Probably true. When K for a reaction is very large, it is certainly true that at equilibrium you will most likely have more products than reactants, but again, if we use outrageously large and small concentrations of individual reactants and/or products, it is mathematically possible to end up with more reactants than products (see the example in the lecture). But again, if we start with "normal" concentrations, we will most likely end up with more products than reactants at equilibrium.

   C. A reasonable but somewhat ambiguous interpretation. The word "favored" does not have a clear, specific meaning.

   D. Likewise, a reasonable but somewhat ambiguous interpretation. The phrase "lies to the right" does not have a clear, specific meaning.

6. **A.** Reaction 1.

   B. Reaction 3.

   C. Reaction 2. The extremely large value for the equilibrium constant tells us that this reaction essentially goes to completion. The concentration of O_2 remaining at equilibrium would be 0.50 M. You started with 1.00 mol of both H_2 and O_2. The reaction essentially goes to completion. The stoichiometry of the reaction says that the entire 1.00 mol of H_2 would be consumed, and at the same time 0.50 mol of O_2 would be consumed, leaving you with 0.50 mol of O_2 in the system after the reaction has essentially gone to completion.

7. **A.** $K = \frac{1}{4.00} = 0.25$. This is true because when you reverse the equation, the new $K = \frac{[A][B]}{[C][D]}$, which is just the reciprocal of the equilibrium constant expression for the forward reaction.

   B. $K = 16.00$. The original K was $\frac{[C][D]}{[A][B]}$. The new K is $\frac{[C]^2[D]^2}{[A]^2[B]^2}$, which is just equal to the original equilibrium constant expression squared.

C. $K = (\frac{1}{4.00})^{\frac{1}{2}} = 0.50$. You have reversed the equation, so the new K will be the reciprocal of the old K, but you also have multiplied the equation by $\frac{1}{2}$, and following what we learned above, this would mean that we now have to take the new K to the $\frac{1}{2}$ power (the square root).

Lecture Twenty-Five
Le Chatelier's Principle—Concentration

1. If a stress is applied
   to a system at equilibrium,
   the system will shift,
   if possible,
   in the direction
   that completely,
   or at least partially,
   alleviates the stress.

2. Stress is defined as a change in the concentration of one of the reactants or products, a change in pressure, or a change in temperature.

3. **A.** Left
    B. The concentrations of C_6H_6 and O_2 would increase.

    The concentration of H_2O would decrease.

    There would be a net increase in the concentration of CO_2. It would decrease as the system shifts but would not be able to get back to where it was originally. You would not be able to completely alleviate this concentration stress.

    C. Nothing

4. **A.** Right
    B. The concentrations of Fe^{2+} and Sn^{4+} would decrease.

    The concentration of Fe^{3+} would increase.

    There would be a net decrease in the concentration of Sn^{2+}.

    C. Nothing.

5. **A.** Left
    B. The concentration of NOBr would increase.

    The concentration of Br_2 would decrease.

    There would be a net increase in the concentration of NO.

    C. Nothing
    D. Right
    E. The concentration of NOBr would decrease.

    The concentration of NO would increase.

    There would be a net decrease in the concentration of Br_2.

    F. Nothing.

6. A. Left

   B. The concentration of OH^- would decrease.

   There would be a net increase in the concentration of H^+.

   The concentration of H_2O would not change, because it is a pure liquid. The amount of water would increase, but not its concentration.

   C. Nothing

7. The molarity of anything is simply the number of moles of that substance contained in 1 L. A liter of water would weigh 1000 g. Since the molar mass of water is 18.0 g/mol, 1 mol water would contain $\frac{1000 \text{ g}}{18.0 \text{ g/mol}} = 55.5$ M.

Lecture Twenty-Six
Le Chatelier—Pressure and Temperature

1. A, B, C, D, and E. F is false because for some substances you can only determine what happens to the amount of the substance, not its concentration, since the pressure change was brought about by changing the volume of the system, which also has an influence on the final concentration. G is false because Le Chatelier's principle can only be applied to a system that has already achieved a state of equilibrium. If a system has not yet achieved equilibrium, there is no way to apply the principle to determine which direction the reaction will proceed.

2. **A.** Right

    B. The concentrations of CO_2 and H_2O would increase.

    The concentration of C_6H_6 would decrease.

    There would be a net increase in the concentration of O_2. It would decrease as the system shifts but would not be able to get back to where it was originally. You would not be able to completely alleviate this concentration stress.

    C. Nothing

    D. Right. If pressure were decreased, the system would want to do the opposite, or increase the pressure. If the system shifts to the right, the number of gaseous molecules in the container would increase, since there are 17 molecules of gaseous reactants but 18 molecules of gaseous products. More gaseous molecules will exert more pressure.

    E. The amounts of CO_2 and H_2O would increase.

    The amounts of C_6H_6 and O_2 would decrease.

    F. Nothing

    G. Left. If temperature is increased, the system would want to decrease the temperature. The reaction as written is exothermic, as indicated by the negative sign in front of ΔH. When an exothermic reaction occurs (like burning a candle in a sealed bottle), the temperature increases, so when an endothermic reaction occurs (like ice melting inside a container), the temperature inside the system will decrease. The reverse reaction is endothermic, so the system would shift to the left.

    H. The concentration of both reactants would increase, while the concentration of both products would decrease.

    I. Decrease. If the system shifts to the left, the concentration of the products (the numerator in the expression for K) would decrease and the concentration of the reactants (the denominator in the expression for K) would increase.

3. **A.** Right

    B. The concentrations of CO and hydrogen would both decrease.

    The concentration of CH_4 would increase.

    There would be a net decrease in the concentration of $H_2O(g)$.

    C. Nothing

    D. Right

    E. The amounts of both reactants would decrease, while the amount of both products would increase.

    F. Nothing

G. Left

H. The concentrations of both reactants would increase. The concentrations of both products would decrease.

I. It would decrease.

4. **A.** It would not shift, because we had not changed the volume. When applying Le Chatelier's principle, we only consider pressure changes brought about by a decrease or increase in volume.

   B. It would shift to the left. The helium itself has nothing to do with the shifting, but if you are going to inject helium into the container but are going to keep the total pressure at 1.88 atm, you are going to have to increase the volume of the container. If you do not, the pressure inside would increase due to the presence of the additional helium gas. Increasing the volume would constitute a decrease in pressure in the Le Chatelier game rules. If the pressure were decreased, the system would want to increase the pressure, so it would shift to the left, where there are more gaseous molecules.

Lecture Twenty-Seven
An Introduction to Equilibrium Problems

1. $K = \frac{[C][D]^2}{[A]^2[B]^3} = \frac{(0.0783)(2.24)^2}{(1.72)^2(0.815)^3} = 0.245$

2. $K = \frac{[H^+][F^-]}{[HF]} = \frac{(1.30 \times 10^{-2})(1.30 \times 10^{-2})}{(0.250)} = 6.76 \times 10^{-4}$

3. $K = \frac{[C]^3[D]}{[A][B]^2} = 4.2 \times 10^{-3}$

   $\frac{(0.15)^3(0.27)}{[A](4.38)^2} = 4.2 \times 10^{-3}$

   $\frac{(0.15)^3(0.27)}{[A](4.38)^2(4.2 \times 10^{-3})}$

   $[A] = \frac{(0.15)^3(0.27)}{(4.38)^2(4.2 \times 10^{-3})}$

   $[A] = 1.13 \times 10^{-2}$

4. $K = \frac{[C]^2[D]}{[A]^2[B]^3} = 7.3 \times 10^{-2}$

   $K = \frac{(4.22)^2(3.19)}{[A]^2(5.11)^3} = 7.3 \times 10^{-2}$

   $(4.22)^2(3.19) = [A]^2(5.11)^3(7.3 \times 10^{-2})$

   $[A]^2 = \frac{(4.22)^2(3.19)}{(5.11)^3(7.3 \times 10^{-2})}$

   $[A]^2 = 5.83$ M

   $[A] = 2.41$ M

5. $K = [Pb^{2+}][I^-]^2 = 7.1 \times 10^{-9}$

   $(0.064)[I^-]^2 = 7.1 \times 10^{-9}$

   $[I^-]^2 = \frac{7.1 \times 10^{-9}}{0.064} = 1.11 \times 10^{-7}$

   $[I^-] = 3.33 \times 10^{-4}$ M

6. $2H_2S(g) \leftrightarrow 2H_2(g) + S_2(g)$

   $K = \frac{[H_2]^2[S_2]}{[H_2S]^2}$

   The real problem is to find the equilibrium concentrations of all 3 substances.

   $[H_2] = 0.38$ M (given)

   $[S_2] = \frac{(0.38 \text{ mol } H_2)(1 \text{ mol } S_2)}{(2 \text{ mol } H_2)} = 0.19$ mol $H_2 = 0.19$ M (1-L container)

   mol H_2S consumed $= 0.38$ mol (since its coefficient is same as the coefficient of H_2)

   mol H_2S remaining $= 1.00 - 0.38 = 0.62$ mol $= 0.62$ M

   $K = \frac{(0.38)^2(0.19)}{(0.62)^2} = 7.1 \times 10^{-2}$

7. $CO(g) + H_2O(g) \leftrightarrow CO_2(g) + H_2(g)$

Again, the real problem is to find the equilibrium concentrations of all of the reactants and products.

$[CO_2]$ = 1.25 M (given)

$[H_2]$ = 1.25 M (same amount will be produced as is produced of CO_2)

CO and H_2O consumed = 1.25 M (all coefficients are 1)

$[CO] = [H_2O]$ = 1.50 − 1.25 = 0.25 M

$K = \frac{[CO_2][H_2]}{[CO][H_2O]} = \frac{(1.25)(1.25)}{(0.25)(0.25)} = 25$

8. $3A + 2B \leftrightarrow C + 5D$

The real problem is once again to find the equilibrium concentrations. First, we find the initial concentrations.

$[A]_0 = \frac{4.00 \, \text{mol}}{2.00 \, \text{L}} = 2.00$ M

$[B]_0 = \frac{5.00 \, \text{mol}}{2.00 \, \text{L}} = 2.50$ M

In doing stoichiometry, we can do molar ratios the same way we do mole ratios.

$[C]$ = 0.35 M (given)

$[D] = (0.35 \, \text{M C})(\frac{5 \, \text{M D}}{1 \, \text{M C}}) = 1.75$ M

mol/L A consumed = $(0.35 \, \text{M C})(\frac{3 \, \text{M A}}{1 \, \text{M C}}) = 1.05$ M

$[A]$ = 2.00 − 1.05 = 0.95 M

mol/L B consumed = $(0.35 \, \text{M C})(\frac{2 \, \text{M B}}{1 \, \text{M C}}) = 0.70$ M

$[B]$ = 2.50 − 0.70 = 1.80 M B

$K = \frac{[C][D]^5}{[A]^3[B]^2} = \frac{(0.35)(1.75)^5}{(0.95)^3(1.80)^2} = 2.07$

Lecture Twenty-Eight
The Self-Ionization of Water

1. The purpose was to show the difference between strong electrolytes, weak electrolytes, and nonelectrolytes. Solutions of nonelectrolytes do not conduct electricity. Solutions of strong electrolytes, assuming they are soluble, are excellent conductors of electricity. Solutions of weak electrolytes conduct electricity, but nowhere near as well as an equivalent solution of a strong electrolyte. In addition, the demonstration showed that pure water is essentially a nonelectrolyte. Any conductivity detected in water is due to substances that are dissolved in the water, typically minerals, which are ionic solids.

2. Electricity is the movement of electrical charge.

3. In a solid material that conducts electricity, like a metal, the moving charges are electrons. In a solution, the moving charges are ions.

4. $2H_2O \leftrightarrow H_3O^+ + OH^-$

   $H_2O \leftrightarrow H^+ + OH^-$

   There is no "correct" equation. Both are commonly used. The first probably more accurately represents what actually exists in solution, since it is not possible for just H^+ to exist in water because H^+ would just be a bare proton. A bare proton cannot exist in water. It would attach itself to a water molecule.

   The second is better for our purposes because it makes it easier to write equations for acid-base reactions and equilibrium constants for many reactions that we will be discussing. In addition, while H^+ is not what actually exists in solution, it is doubtful that H_3O^+ is what actually exists anyway. The actual situation is probably quite complex.

5. If we use the equation $H_2O(l) \leftrightarrow H^+ + OH^-$

   $K_w = [H^+][OH^-] = 1.00 \times 10^{-14}$

   K_w is called the ion product of water.

6. A, B, C, D, E, F, and H

7. $[H^+][OH^-] = 1.00 \times 10^{-14}$

   $(10^{-9})[OH^-] = 1.00 \times 10^{-14}$

   $[OH^-] = \frac{10^{-14}}{10^{-9}} = 10^{-5}$ M

8. $[H^+][OH^-] = 1.00 \times 10^{-14}$

   $[H^+](9.2 \times 10^{-3}) = 1.00 \times 10^{-14}$

   $[H^+] = \frac{1.00 \times 10^{-14}}{9.2 \times 10^{-3}} = 1.09 \times 10^{-12}$ M

9. $[H^+][OH^-] = 1.00 \times 10^{-14}$

   $[H^+](7.8 \times 10^{-4}) = 1.00 \times 10^{-14}$

   $[H^+] = \frac{1.00 \times 10^{-14}}{7.8 \times 10^{-4}} = 1.3 \times 10^{-11}$ M

10. Let $x = [OH^-]$. Then $[H^+] = 3x$, since the problem states that the concentration of hydrogen ion is 3 times the concentration of hydroxide ion.

$$[H^+][OH^-] = 1.00 \times 10^{-14}$$

$$(3x)(x) = 1.00 \times 10^{-14}$$

$$3x^2 = 1.00 \times 10^{-14}$$

$$x^2 = 3.33 \times 10^{-15}$$

$$x = 5.77 \times 10^{-8}$$

$$[H^+] = (3)(5.77 \times 10^{-8}) = 1.73 \times 10^{-7} \text{ M}$$

$$[OH^-] = 5.77 \times 10^{-8} \text{ M}$$

11. A. $[H^+][OH^-] = 1.471 \times 10^{-14}$

Let x = mol/L H_2O that ionize.

$$(x)(x) = 1.471 \times 10^{-14}$$

$$x^2 = 1.471 \times 10^{-14}$$

$$x = 1.213 \times 10^{-7} \text{ M}$$

$$[H^+] = [OH^-] = 1.213 \times 10^{-7} \text{ M}$$

B. $pH = -\log[H^+] = -\log(1.213 \times 10^{-7}) = -(-6.92) = 6.92$

C. It is neutral, despite its pH being less than 7. There is nothing magical about a pH of 7. The only reason this number represents a neutral solution at room temperature is because at 25°C this is the pH at which the concentrations of hydrogen ion and hydroxide are equal to each other, both being equal to 10^{-7} M. At higher temperatures water is more highly ionized. This means that both the hydrogen and hydroxide ion concentrations are higher. This means that both the pH and pOH are lower than 7. But since the concentrations of these 2 ions are still equal to each other, the solution is still neutral.

Lecture Twenty-Nine
Strong Acids and Bases—General Properties

1. $pH = -\log[H^+] = -\log(3.74 \times 10^{-12}) = -(-11.43) = 11.43$

2. $[H^+][OH^-] = 1.00 \times 10^{-14}$

   $[H^-](5.87 \times 10^{-6}) = 1.00 \times 10^{-14}$

   $[H^+] = \frac{1.00 \times 10^{-14}}{5.87 \times 10^{-6}} = 1.70 \times 10^{-9}$ M

   $pH = -\log(1.70 \times 10^{-9}) = -(-8.77) = 8.77$

3. $[H^+] = 10^{-13}$ M

4. $[H^+] = 10^{-7.49} = 3.24 \times 10^{-8}$ M

5. We will work this problem by both the methods shown in the lecture. In later problems only 1 method will be shown.

   Method 1:

   $[H^+][OH^-] = 1.00 \times 10^{-14}$

   $(4.84 \times 10^{-8})[OH^-] = 1.00 \times 10^{-14}$

   $[OH^-] = \frac{1.00 \times 10^{-14}}{4.84 \times 10^{-8}} = 2.07 \times 10^{-7}$ M

   $pOH = -\log[OH^-] = -\log(2.07 \times 10^{-7}) = -(-6.68) = 6.68$

   Method 2:

   $pH = -\log[H^+] = -\log(4.84 \times 10^{-8}) = -(7.32) = 7.32$

   $pH + pOH = 14$

   $pOH = 14 - pH = 14 - 7.32 = 6.68$

6. An acid is a substance that produces H^+ in aqueous solution. A base is a substance that produces OH^- in aqueous solution.

7. A strong acid is an acid that is essentially 100% ionized in aqueous solution.

8. Most acids are weak acids. There are only 6 common strong acids that are typically encountered in a high school chemistry course.

9. HCl, hydrochloric acid

   HBr, hydrobromic acid

   HI, hydriodic acid

   HNO_3, nitric acid

   $HClO_4$, perchloric acid

   H_2SO_4, sulfuric acid

10. $HMwO_5 \leftrightarrow H^+ + MwO_5^-$

Lecture Thirty
Solving Strong Acid and Base Problems

1. $\frac{5.28 \text{ g HCl}}{36.5 \text{ g/mol}} = 0.1447$ mol HCl

   $[\text{HCl}] = \frac{0.1447 \text{ mol}}{0.396 \text{ mL}} = 0.3654$ M

   $\text{HCl} \rightarrow \text{H}^+ + \text{Cl}^-$

   $[\text{H}^+] = 0.3654$ M

   $\text{pH} = -\log[\text{H}^+] = -\log(0.3654) = -(-0.437) = 0.437$

   $[\text{H}^+][\text{OH}^-] = 1.00 \times 10^{-14}$

   $(0.3654)[\text{OH}^-] = 1.00 \times 10^{-14}$

   $[\text{OH}^-] = \frac{1.00 \times 10^{-14}}{0.3654} = 2.74 \times 10^{-14}$

   $\text{pOH} = -\log[\text{OH}^-] = -\log(2.74 \times 10^{-14}) = -(-13.56) = 13.56$

2. $\frac{23.83 \text{ g HNO}_3}{63.0 \text{ g/mol}} = 0.3783$ mol HNO$_3$

   $[\text{HNO}_3] = \frac{0.3783 \text{ mol}}{5.24 \text{ L}} = 0.07219$ M

   $\text{HNO}_3 \rightarrow \text{H}^+ + \text{NO}_3^-$

   $[\text{H}^+] = 0.07219$ M

   $\text{pH} = -\log[\text{H}^+] = -\log(0.07219) = -(-1.14) = 1.14$

   $\text{pH} + \text{pOH} = 14$

   $\text{pOH} = 14 - \text{pH} = 14 - 1.14 = 12.86$

   $[\text{OH}^-] = 10^{-12.86} = 1.38 \times 10^{-13}$ M

3. Most bases are strong.

4. Most bases that are encountered in a high school chemistry course are what we call metallic hydroxides.

5. **A.** $\text{LiOH} \rightarrow \text{Li}^+ + \text{OH}^-$

   B. $\text{Ca(OH)}_2 \rightarrow \text{Ca}^{2+} + 2\text{OH}^-$

6. The alkali metals—Li, Na, K, Rb, and Cs—which all have a charge of +1. This is the first column in the periodic table.

   The alkaline earth metals—Mg, Ca, Sr, and Ba—which all have a charge of +2. This is the second column in the periodic table.

7. $\dfrac{9.16 \text{ g}}{40.0 \text{ g/mol}} = 0.229$ mol NaOH

[NaOH] $= \dfrac{0.229 \text{ mol}}{0.582 \text{ L}} = 0.3935$ M

$NaOH \rightarrow Na^+ + OH^-$

$[OH^-] = 0.3935$ M

$pOH = -\log(0.3935) = -(-0.405) = 0.405$

$[H^+][OH^-] = 1.00 \times 10^{-14}$

$[H^+](0.3935) = 1.00 \times 10^{-14}$

$[H^+] = \dfrac{1.00 \times 10^{-14}}{0.3935} = 2.54 \times 10^{-14}$

$pH = -\log(2.54 \times 10^{-14}) = -(-13.595) = 13.595$

8. $\dfrac{7.77 \text{ g}}{171.3 \text{ g/mol}} = 0.04536$ mol $Ba(OH)_2$

$[Ba(OH)_2] = \dfrac{0.04536 \text{ mol}}{0.777 \text{ L}} = 0.0584$ M

$Ba(OH)_2 \rightarrow Ba^{2+} + 2OH^-$

$[OH^-] = 2(0.0584) = 0.117$ M

$pOH = -\log(0.117) = -(-0.933) = 0.933$

$pH = 14 - 0.933 = 13.067$

9. The key ideas here are that the H^+ comes from the HCl and the OH^- comes from the NaOH. Each mole of HCl will produce 1 mol H^+ ($HCl \rightarrow H^+ + Cl^-$) and each mole of NaOH will produce 1 mol OH^- ($NaOH \rightarrow Na^+ + OH^-$).

mol H^+ = (1.22 mol/L)(0.03800 L) = 0.04636 mol H^+

mol OH^- = (1.44 mol/L)(0.04500 L) = 0.06480 mol OH^-

Since H^+ and OH^- react in a 1:1 mol ratio, the OH^- is in excess, and the amount of OH^- remaining after the reaction is as follows:

0.06480 − 0.04636 = 0.01844 mol OH^-

After mixing, the total volume is 38.00 + 45.00 = 83.00 mL

$[OH^-] = \dfrac{0.01844 \text{ mol}}{0.08300 \text{ L}} = 0.2222$ M

$pOH = -\log(0.2222) = 0.653$

$pH = 14 - 0.653 = 13.347$

Lecture Thirty-One
Weak Acids and Bases

1. $HClO_2 \leftrightarrow H^+ + ClO_2^-$

   $K = [H^+][ClO_2^-]/[HClO_2]$

2. A weak acid, by definition, is only slightly ionized in aqueous solution under normal conditions and concentrations. Therefore, solutions of weak acids have relatively low concentrations of the product ions and relatively high concentrations of the reactant acid molecules. Since equilibrium constant expressions involve the concentration of the products over the concentration of the reactants, K_a for any weak acid would have to have a small value.

3. HCl, HSO_4^-, HF, HNO_2, $HC_2H_3O_2$, and HCN

4. $HBrO \leftrightarrow H^+ + BrO^-$

   $K_a = \frac{[H^+][BrO^-]}{[HBrO]} = 2.5 \times 10^{-9}$

   Let x = mol/L HBrO that ionize.

   $\frac{(x)(x)}{1.00 - x} = 2.5 \times 10^{-9}$

   Assume x is negligible compared to 1.00. We can assume x is negligible because HBrO is a weak acid, as indicated by the small numerical value for its ionization constant, and therefore would only be slightly ionized in aqueous solution.

   $\frac{(x)(x)}{1.00} = 2.5 \times 10^{-9}$

   $x^2 = 2.5 \times 10^{-9}$

   $x = 5.0 \times 10^{-5}$

   $[H^+] = [BrO^-] = 5.0 \times 10^{-5}$ M

   [HBrO] = 1.00 M (technically 1.00 − 0.00005, but the 0.00005 is so small as to be insignificant here)

   $[H^+][OH^-] = 1.00 \times 10^{-14}$

   $(5.0 \times 10^{-5})[OH^-] = 1.00 \times 10^{-14}$

   $[OH^-] = \frac{1.00 \times 10^{-14}}{5.0 \times 10^{-5}} = 2.0 \times 10^{-10}$ M

   $pH = -\log[H^+] = -\log(5.0 \times 10^{-5}) = -(-4.30) = 4.30$

   $pH + pOH = 14$

   $pOH = 14 - pH = 14 - 4.30 = 9.70$

   % ionization $= \frac{5.0 \times 10^{-5}}{1.00} \times 100 = 0.0050\%$

5. $HOCN \leftrightarrow H^+ + OCN^-$

$K_a = \frac{[H^+][OCN^-]}{[HOCN]} = 3.5 \times 10^{-4}$

Let x = mol/L HOCN that ionize.

$\frac{(x)(x)}{0.75 - x} = 3.5 \times 10^{-4}$

Assume x is negligible compared to 0.75.

$\frac{(x)(x)}{0.75} = 3.5 \times 10^{-4}$

$x^2 = (0.75)(3.5 \times 10^{-4}) = 2.625 \times 10^{-4}$

$x = 1.62 \times 10^{-2}$

$[H^+] = [OCN^-] = 1.62 \times 10^{-2}$ M

$[HOCN] = 0.75 - 0.0162 = 0.73$ M (but can be approximated as 0.75 M)

$[H^+][OH^-] = 1.00 \times 10^{-14}$

$(1.62 \times 10^{-2})[OH^-] = 1.00 \times 10^{-14}$

$[OH^-] = \frac{1.00 \times 10^{-14}}{1.62 \times 10^{-2}} = 6.17 \times 10^{-13}$ M

$pH = -\log[H^+] = -\log(1.62 \times 10^{-2}) = -(-1.79) = 1.79$

$pH + pOH = 14$

$pOH = 14 - pH = 14 - 1.79 = 12.21$

%ionization $= \frac{1.62 \times 10^{-2}}{0.75} \times 100 = 2.16\%$

6. $K_b = \frac{[NH_4^+][OH^-]}{[NH_3]} = 1.8 \times 10^{-5}$

Let x = mol/L NH_3 that ionize.

$\frac{(x)(x)}{0.370 - x} = 1.8 \times 10^{-5}$

Assume x is negligible compared to 0.370.

$\frac{(x)(x)}{0.370} = 1.8 \times 10^{-5}$

$x^2 = 6.66 \times 10^{-6}$

$x = 2.58 \times 10^{-3}$

$[OH^-] = 2.58 \times 10^{-3}$ M (Remember, this is a base, not an acid.)

$pOH = -\log(2.58 \times 10^{-3}) = -(-2.59) = 2.59$

What a coincidence! The pOH came out to be almost equal to the 2.58 number in the concentration! Honestly, it was just a coincidence. I did not plan this to happen.

$pH = 14 - 2.59 = 11.41$

%ionization $= \frac{2.58 \times 10^{-3}}{0.370} \times 100 = 0.697\%$

7. This was a trick problem. You can completely ignore any H^+ coming from the $HC_2H_3O_2$. $HC_2H_3O_2$ is a weak acid. The amount of H^+ coming from this acid will be negligible compared to the amount coming from the HCl. HCl is one of our 6 strong acids. Therefore, the concentration of H^+ in the solution will just be about 0.50 M, since you end up with 0.500 mol of HCl in a total volume of 1.00 L. Consequently, pH $= -\log 0.50 = 0.30$. If you actually wanted to do the calculation, you would just set up the equilibrium constant expression for $HC_2H_3O_2$ as follows.

$$K_a = \frac{[H^+][C_2H_3O_2^-]}{[HC_2H_3O_2]}$$

You would let $x =$ mol/L $HC_2H_3O_2$ that ionize, but the total concentration of H^+ in the solution would equal what came from the HCl, 0.50 M, plus what came from the $HC_2H_3O_2$, x. The equilibrium constant expression that you would end up solving would be as follows.

$$\frac{(0.50 + x)(x)}{0.50 - x} = 1.8 \times 10^{-5}$$

When you neglect x compared to 0.50, and then solve for x, it just comes out to be 1.8×10^{-5}. Since the total $[H^+] = 0.50 + x$, but x is so small you just get $[H^+] = 0.50$ M—which is what we knew would be true without having to solve any equation.

Lecture Thirty-Two

Titrating Acids and Bases

1. When a strong acid reacts with a strong base, the reaction that occurs is just the hydrogen ions from the acid reacting with the hydroxide ions from the base. The equation for this reaction is just $H^+ + OH^- \leftrightarrow H_2O$. The equilibrium constant for this reaction is just the reciprocal of the equilibrium constant for the ionization of water, so its numerical value would be

$$\frac{1}{1.00 \times 10^{-14}}$$

or 1.00×10^{14}. This is such a large value that we can say this neutralization reaction goes to completion for all practical purposes.

2. The equivalence point is the point in the titration where you have added the correct amount of base to just neutralize the amount of acid present in the solution, or vice versa. The end point is typically the point in the titration where whatever indicator you are using changes color and you therefore end the titration.

3. The end point and the equivalence point typically differ from each other by an insignificant amount in a well-designed titration experiment. Ensuring that an experiment is well designed can at times be somewhat complex, depending on the actual titration being performed, but titration experiments found in commercial laboratory manuals are assumed to meet such a criterion.

4. Although not the best definition, for the time being we have defined an indicator as a substance that is one color in an acidic solution and a different color in a basic solution. Two indicators commonly used in high school laboratories are litmus and phenolphthalein. Litmus is red (more like pink) in an acid and blue (or something kind of like blue) in a base. Phenolphthalein is colorless in an acid and red (usually looking more pink) in a base.

5. **A.** After you wash a burette, there is water on the inside. If you just filled the burette with the solution it was going to hold, this solution would be diluted by the water left inside the burette. This would alter the concentration of the solution of acid or base you were using in the titration. In the case of the acid, you would end up determining the concentration of this diluted acid rather than the acid whose concentration you were actually trying to determine. In the case of the base, which would be your standard solution, you would be titrating with a base whose concentration was different from the concentration value you would be using in your calculations.

   B. If you do not drain a bit of the solution out of the burettes, the first little bit of solution that you think you are adding to the reaction vessel is used to just fill the tip of the burette and never actually makes it into the reaction vessel. This makes you think that you have added more of the solution to the reaction vessel than you actually have.

   C. The reason you add some distilled water to the reaction vessel is simply to give you a larger total volume of solution in the vessel. The titration will work if you do not do this, but the volume of acid and base used in a titration is usually so small that you end up with just a relatively small volume of solution in a rather large vessel. It is easier to mix, swirl, and so forth if you make the volume of the solution a bit larger. That is the only reason you add the distilled water.

   D. You need to keep the solution thoroughly mixed. As you add the base, local areas of the solution will be completely neutralized, changing the color of the indicator in these areas. But you need to neutralize the entire solution, so it must be thoroughly mixed, which is usually accomplished by swirling the solution, since the reaction vessel is typically an Erlenmeyer flask, which lends itself to swirling.

E. Although our original plan was to carefully add base until a good end point is achieved, you can "back-titrate" if you should overshoot the end point, and if you then overshoot the end point going in the opposite direction, you can add more base. It does not matter how the end point is arrived at. An end point is an end point. Just remember to take the new "final" reading on your acid or base burette.

6. A. Volume of acid used $= 44.25 - 1.55 = 42.70$ mL

Volume of base used $= 32.50 - 0.75 = 31.75$ mL

The acid is less concentrated than the base, so its molarity will be less than 0.383 M.

We know this because at the end point (equivalence point, we assume), the number of moles of HCl is equal to the number of moles of NaOH we added. This is true because the molecular equation for the reaction is HCl + NaOH $\rightarrow$ NaCl + H_2O. Since the number of moles of acid was contained in a larger volume than the base (42.70 mL versus 31.75 mL), the acid must be less concentrated than the base.

B. mol NaOH $= (0.383$ mol/L$)(0.03175$ L$) = 0.01216$ mol NaOH

mol HCl $= 0.01216$ mol (moles of acid and base are equal)

[HCl] $= \frac{0.01216 \text{ mol}}{0.04270 \text{ L}} = 0.285$ M

7. The catch in this problem is that sulfuric acid has 2 hydrogens that must be neutralized. The balanced equation for the reaction that occurs is as follows:

$H_2SO_4 + 2NaOH \leftrightarrow Na_2SO_4 + 2H_2O$

Consequently, the number of moles of acid present in the unknown solution is only half the number of moles of NaOH that were added.

Volume of H_2SO_4 used $= 22.25 - 0.15 = 22.10$ mL

Volume of NaOH used $= 46.50 - 1.05 = 45.45$ mL

mol NaOH used $= (0.558$ mol/L$)(0.04545$ L$) = 0.02536$ mol

mol H_2SO_4 used $= \frac{0.02536}{2} = 0.01268$ mol

[H_2SO_4] $= \frac{0.01268 \text{ mol}}{0.02210 \text{ L}} = 0.574$ M

8. A. It works because when you multiply the molarity of a solution times the volume of the solution (in liters), you get the number of moles of acid or base, and at the equivalence point the moles of acid and base must be equal to each other. In actual practice, the volumes are typically plugged in units of milliliters, for convenience, which is fine, since we have the same volume units on both side of the equation, so converting them to liters would not accomplish anything.

B. It will not work if you have a reaction like the one in the previous problem, where the mole ratio between the acid and base is not 1:1. In cases like this, the number of moles of acid and base are not equal to each other at the equivalence point.

C. It is not needed. Why use a special formula rather than just think through and understand what you are doing, especially when the special formula does not always work anyway?

Lecture Thirty-Three
Titration Curves and Indicators

1. B, E, F, H, and I

2. An indicator is a weak acid or base whose molecular form is one color while its ionic form is a different color.

3. Indicators do not have any kind of special property that causes them to change color rapidly around the equivalence point of a titration. The reason they change color so rapidly is simply because the ratio of the 2 forms of the indicator—the molecular form and the ionic form—depends on the concentration of hydrogen ions in the solution. At the equivalence point of a titration, the concentration of hydrogen ions changes dramatically, perhaps by a factor of about 1 million, which in turn causes the ratio of the 2 forms of the indicator to also change by this factor. This is what causes the dramatic and abrupt color change, not some special property of the indicator itself.

4. Different indicators change color over a small pH range on either side of the numerical value for $-\log K_a$ for that indicator. Since different indicators have different values for their ionization constants, they will change color over different pH ranges.

5. It should change color around a pH $= -\log(8.3 \times 10^{-6})$, or 5.08.

6. When you titrate a strong acid with a weak base, the solution at the equivalence point is still somewhat acidic, and vice versa.

7. We want to select an indicator that will change color at or close to the equivalence point of the titration.
    A. **b**, Litmus: When we titrate a strong acid like HNO_3 with a strong base like NaOH, the equivalence point will occur at a pH of 7, so we select an indicator like litmus, which changes color at a pH of about 7.
    B. **c**, Alizarin yellow: When we titrate a weak acid like $HC_2H_3O_2$ with a strong base like KOH, we expect the pH at the equivalence point to be above 7 ("me weak acid; ME STRONG BASE"). Alizarin yellow changes color over a pH range from 10.0 to 12.0.
    C. **a**, Methyl red: When we titrate a weak base like NH_3 with a strong acid like HCl, we expect the pH at the equivalence point to be below 7 ("me weak base; ME STRONG ACID"). Methyl red changes color over a pH range from 4.4 to 6.2.

8. Student B had better not agree with Student A. It will take both students 50.0 mL of NaOH to reach the equivalence point of their titrations. Although there is very little H^+ in a solution of a weak acid like HClO, as pointed out in the lecture, as you neutralize the H^+ that is present in the solution, more of the HClO will ionize to try to replace the H^+ that was consumed, as is predicted by Le Chatelier's principle. The better plan is to just to have each student neutralize 25.0 mL of their respective acids. Each student will then only require 25.0 mL of the NaOH, so there will be enough for both of them, assuming they do not mess up the titration.

9. A. False. Since our starting solution was a weak acid and therefore not as highly ionized, the concentration of H^+ in our initial acid solution would not be as great as it would be in a strong acid, so the starting pH would be a bit higher.
    B. True
    C. False

D. True. The old "ME STRONG BASE; me weak acid" thing.

E. False

F. True

10. The first thing to realize is that the equation given only shows the essential reacting species. The K^+ and Na^+ really have nothing to do with the actual reaction that takes place between the KHP and the NaOH. The next thing to realize is that KHP and NaOH react with each other in a 1:1 mole ratio. For every mole of KHP you have, you need 1 mol NaOH to neutralize it. Then you have to realize that even though the K^+ has nothing to do with the reaction, it must be included when you determine the molar mass of the KHP, since it is present in the KHP when you weigh out the 4.878-g sample.

$KHC_8H_4O_4$ = 204.1 g/mol

$$\frac{2.878 \text{ g } KHC_8H_4O_4}{204.1 \text{ g/mol}} = 0.0141 \text{ mol } KHC_8H_4O_4$$

mol NaOH = 0.0141 mol (reacts with $KHC_8H_4O_4$ in a 1:1 mole ratio)

$$[NaOH] = \frac{0.0141 \text{ mol}}{0.02365 \text{ L}} = 0.596 \text{ M}$$

Lecture Thirty-Four
Solubility Equilibria—Principles, Problems

1. In all equilibrium systems we have discussed to this point, the equilibrium constant was always satisfied. But this is not necessarily true for solubility equilibria. The solubility product expression K_{sp} is only satisfied if the solution is saturated.

2. **A.** $K_{sp} = [Ag^+][I^-]$

    B. $K_{sp} = [Ca^{2+}][SO_4^{2-}]$

    C. $K_{sp} = [Ag^+]^2[CO_3^{2-}]$

    D. $K_{sp} = [Li^+]^3[PO_4^{3-}]$

    E. $K_{sp} = [Hg_2^{2+}][Cl^-]^2$

    F. $K_{sp} = [Sr^{2+}]^3[AsO_4^{3-}]^2$

3. Solubility refers to how much of a substance can be dissolved in a given amount of water or solution. Using the units we have been working with, this would be the number of moles of a substance that could be dissolved in a liter of solution; this is also called the molar solubility. The solubility product, on the other hand, is just the numerical value of the solubility product expression in a saturated solution.

4. $PbSO_4(s) \leftrightarrow Pb^{2+} + SO_4^{2-}$

    $\qquad\qquad x \qquad\quad x \qquad x \qquad$ [where x = mol/L $PbSO_4$ that dissolve (the molar solubility)]

    $K_{sp} = [Pb^{2+}][SO_4^{2-}] = 1.6 \times 10^{-8}$

    $(x)(x) = 1.6 \times 10^{-8}$

    $x = 1.26 \times 10^{-4}$

    Molar solubility = 1.26×10^{-4} M

5. $Fe(OH)_3(s) \leftrightarrow Fe^{3+} + 3OH^-$

    $\qquad\qquad x \qquad\quad x \qquad 3x \qquad$ [where x = mol/L $Fe(OH)_3$ that dissolve (molar solubility)]

    $K_{sp} = [Fe^{3+}][OH^-]^3$

    $(x)(3x)^3 = 4 \times 10^{-38}$

    $(x)(27x^3) = 4 \times 10^{-38}$

    $27x^4 = 4 \times 10^{-38}$

    $x^4 = \frac{4 \times 10^{-38}}{27} = 1.48 \times 10^{-39}$

    $x = 2 \times 10^{-10}$

    So molar solubility = 2×10^{-10} M

6. $Sr_3(AsO_4)_2(s) \leftrightarrow 3Sr^{2+} + AsO_4^{3-}$

$$x \qquad 3x \qquad 2x \qquad \text{[where } x = \text{mol/L } Sr_3(AsO_4)_2(s) \text{ that dissolve]}$$

$K_{sp} = [Sr^{2+}]^3[AsO_4^{3-}]^2 = 4.29 \times 10^{-19}$

$(3x)^3(2x)^2 = 4.29 \times 10^{-19}$

$(27x^3)(4x^2) = 4.29 \times 10^{-19}$

$108x^5 = 4.29 \times 10^{-19}$

$x^5 = \frac{4.29 \times 10^{-19}}{108} = 3.972 \times 10^{-21}$

$x = 8.31 \times 10^{-5}$

Molar solubility $= 8.31 \times 10^{-5}$ M

7. $BaSO_4(s) \leftrightarrow Ba^{2+} + SO_4^{2-}$

$K_{sp} = [Ba^{2+}][SO_4^{2-}]$

$K_{sp} = (1.05 \times 10^{-5})(1.05 \times 10^{-5})$

$K_{sp} = 1.1 \times 10^{-10}$

8. $Ag_2CO_3(s) \leftrightarrow 2Ag^+ + CO_3^{2-}$

From the stoichiometry of the reaction:

$[Ag^+] = 2(1.27 \times 10^{-4}) = 2.54 \times 10^{-4}$ M

$[CO_3^{2-}] = 1.27 \times 10^{-4}$ M

$K_{sp} = [Ag^+]^2[CO_3^{2-}] = (2.54 \times 10^{-4})^2(1.27 \times 10^{-4}) = 8.2 \times 10^{-12}$

9. $M_3X_4(s) \leftrightarrow 3M^{4+} + 4X^{3-}$

$$x \qquad 3x \qquad 4x \qquad\qquad \text{[where } x = \text{mol/L } M_3X_4 \text{ that dissolve]}$$

$K_{sp} = [M^{4+}]^3[X^{3-}]^4 = 8.2 \times 10^{-24}$

$(3x)^3(4x)^4 = 8.2 \times 10^{-24}$

$(27x^3)(256x^4) = 8.2 \times 10^{-24}$

$6912x^7 = 8.2 \times 10^{-24}$

$x^7 = 1.18 \times 10^{-27}$

$x = 1.42 \times 10^{-4}$

Molar solubility $= 1.48 \times 10^{-4}$ M

10. No. This would be true if they had the same general form for their solubility product expressions, but if the 2 compounds have formulas with differing subscripts, the concentration terms in their solubility product expressions would have different exponents. This means that it could turn out that the product with the smaller value for K_{sp} might actually have a higher molar solubility. You would not know until you did the numerical calculations.

Lecture Thirty-Five
Solubility Equilibria—Common Ion Effect

1. The common ion effect refers to the shifting of an equilibrium system caused by the addition or presence of a ion contained in the system from a source other than the equilibrium system itself. Le Chatelier's principle predicts this effect. If, for example, you were to add some Cl^- or Ag^+ to a saturated solution of AgCl(s), $AgCl(s) \leftrightarrow Ag^+ + Cl^-$, from a source separate from the AgCl itself (like NaCl or $AgNO_3$), Le Chatelier's principle predicts that since this would cause an increase in the concentration of either the Cl^- or the Ag^+, and since the system would want to undo this stress, it would shift to the left, precipitating out some AgCl. This means that less AgCl remains dissolved, which of course means that its solubility is less than it was in pure water.

2. **A.** $Pb(NO_3)_2(s) \leftrightarrow Pb^{2+} + 2NO_3^-$

    Since lead nitrate dissolves completely, and from the stoichiometry of the reaction $[Pb^{2+}] = 0.25$ M from the $Pb(NO_3)_2$, The total concentration of Pb^{2+} will be equal to what we got from the $Pb(NO_3)_2$ (0.25 M) plus what we got from the $PbSO_4$ (x mol/L). The concentration of SO_4^{2-} will just be x mol/L.

    $PbSO_4(s) \leftrightarrow Pb^{2+} + SO_4^{2-}$

    $\quad x \quad\quad 0.25 + x \quad x \quad\quad$ [where x = mol/L $PbSO_4$ that dissolve]

    $[Pb^{2+}][SO_4^{2-}] = 1.6 \times 10^{-8}$

    $(0.25 + x)(x) = 1.6 \times 10^{-8}$

    Assume x is negligible compared to 0.25.

    $(0.25)(x) = 1.6 \times 10^{-8}$

    $x = \frac{1.60 \times 10^{-8}}{0.25} = 6.4 \times 10^{-8}$

    Molar solubility = 6.4×10^{-8} M

    B. It is smaller. In pure water, the solubility of lead sulfate was 1.26×10^{-4} M. In 0.25 M lead nitrate, the solubility of lead sulfate was only 6.4×10^{-8} M, illustrating the common ion effect.

3. **A.** $Ca(OH)_2(s) \leftrightarrow Ca^{2+} + 2OH^-$

    $\quad\quad\quad x \quad\quad x \quad\quad 2x \quad\quad$ [where x = mol/L $Ca(OH)_2$ that dissolve]

    $[Ca^{2+}][OH^-]^2 = 5.5 \times 10^{-6}$

    $(x)(2x)^2 = 5.5 \times 10^{-6}$

    $(x)(4x^2) = 5.5 \times 10^{-6}$

    $4x^3 = 5.5 \times 10^{-6}$

    $x^3 = \frac{5.5 \times 10^{-6}}{4} = 1.375 \times 10^{-6}$

    $x = 1.12x \times 10^{-2}$

    Molar solubility = 1.12×10^{-2} M

B. $Ba(OH)_2(s) \rightarrow Ba^{2+} + 2OH^-$

Since the $Ba(OH)_2$ dissolves completely, from the stoichiometry of the reaction $[OH^-] = 2(0.77) = 1.54$ M from the $Ba(OH)_2$.

$[Ca^{2+}][OH^-]^2 = 5.5 \times 10^{-6}$

$(x)(1.54 + 2x)^2 = 5.5 \times 10^{-6}$

The logic behind the above statement is that you get x mol/L Ca^{2+} and $2x$ mol/L OH^- from the $Ca(OH)_2$, plus another 1.54 mol/L OH^- from the $Ba(OH)_2$.

Neglect $2x$ compared to 1.54.

$(x)(1.54)^2 = 5.5 \times 10^{-6}$

$(x)(2.3716) = 5.5 \times 10^{-6}$

$x = \frac{5.5 \times 10^{-6}}{2.3716} = 2.32 \times 10^{-6}$

Molar solubility $= 2.32 \times 10^{-6}$ M

4. A. $Mg(OH)_2(s) \leftrightarrow Mg^{2+} + 2OH^-$

$\qquad\qquad\quad x \qquad\quad x \qquad 2x \quad$ [where $x =$ mol/L $Mg(OH)_2$ that dissolve]

$[Mg^{2+}][OH^-] = 1.8 \times 10^{-11}$

$(x)(2x)^2 = 1.8 \times 10^{-11}$

$(x)(4x^2) = 1.8 \times 10^{-11}$

$4x^3 = 1.8 \times 10^{-11}$

$x^3 = \frac{1.8 \times 10^{-11}}{4} = 4.5 \times 10^{-12}$

$x = 1.65 \times 10^{-4}$

Molar solubility $= 1.65 \times 10^{-4}$ M

B. $pOH = 14 - pH = 14 - 11.22 = 2.78$

$[OH^-] = 10^{-2.78} = 1.66 \times 10^{-3}$ M

Let $x =$ mol/L of $Mg(OH)_2$ that dissolve (the molar solubility).

$[Mg^{2+}][OH^-]^2 = 1.8 \times 10^{-11}$

$(x)(1.66 \times 10^{-3} + 2x)^2 = 1.8 \times 10^{-11}$

Assume $2x$ is negligible compared to 1.66×10^{-3}.

Note: 1.66×10^{-3} is a rather small number, but 1.8×10^{-11} is a pretty small value also.

$(x)(1.66 \times 10^{-3})^2 = 1.8 \times 10^{-11}$

$(x)(2.7556 \times 10^{-6}) = 1.8 \times 10^{-11}$

$x = \frac{1.8 \times 10^{-11}}{2.7556 \times 10^{-6}} = 6.53 \times 10^{-6}$

Molar solubility $= 6.54 \times 10^{-6}$ M

Note: $(2)(6.54 \times 10^{-6})$ is small enough compared to 1.66×10^{-3} that our assumption about x was valid.

5. A. $Bi_2S_3(s) \leftrightarrow 2Bi^{3+} + 3S^{2-}$

         x $2x$ $3x$ [where x = mol/L Bi_2S_3 that dissolve]

$[Bi^{3+}]^2[S^{2-}]^3 = 1 \times 10^{-97}$

$(2x)^2(3x)^3 = 1 \times 10^{-97}$

$(4x^2)(27x^3) = 1 \times 10^{-97}$

$108x^5 = 1 \times 10^{-97}$

$x^5 = \frac{1 \times 10^{-97}}{108} = 9.259 \times 10^{-100}$ (Will your calculator do this?)

$x = 1.56 \times 10^{-20}$

Molar solubility = 1.56×10^{-20} M

B. $Na_2S(s) \rightarrow 2Na^+ + S^{2-}$

Let x = mol/L of Bi_2S_3 that dissolve.

$[Bi^{3+}]^2[S^{2-}]^3 = 1 \times 10^{-97}$

$(2x)^2(0.50 + 3x)^3 = 1 \times 10^{-97}$

Assume $3x$ is negligible compared to 0.50.

$(2x)^2(0.50)^3 = 1 \times 10^{-97}$

$(4x^2)(0.125) = 1 \times 10^{-97}$

$x^2 = \frac{1 \times 10^{-97}}{(4)(0.125)} = 2 \times 10^{-97}$

$x = 4.47 \times 10^{-49}$

Molar solubility = 4.47×10^{-49} M (carrying a few unjustified digits in our answer)

$Bi_2S_3 = 514.26$ g/mol

$(4.47 \times 10^{-49}$ mol/L$)(514.26$ g/mol$) = 2.3 \times 10^{-46}$ g/L

C. $(4.47 \times 10^{-49}$ mol/L$)(6.02 \times 10^{23}$ formula units/mol$) = 2.69 \times 10^{-25}$ formula units/L

D. Using our answer from B, if there are 2.3×10^{-46} g/L, then there would be $\frac{1}{2.3 \times 10^{-46} \text{ g}} = 4.34 \times 10^{45}$ L/g!!! To give you some perspective on this, the volume of the world's oceans is about 1.4×10^{21} L, according to a few websites. This means that it would take about $\frac{4.34 \times 10^{45} \text{ L/g}}{1.4 \times 10^{21} \text{ L/ocean}}$, or about 2.2×10^{24} of Earth's oceans filled with 0.50 M Na_2S to dissolve 1 g Bi_2S_3! Needless to say, problems like this may be fun to solve, but they are pretty far removed from reality.

Lecture Thirty-Six
Putting It All Together

1. $\frac{9.29 \text{ L}}{22.414 \text{ L/mol}} = 0.414 \text{ mol SO}_2$

$(0.414 \text{ mol})(6.02 \times 10^{23} \text{ molecules/mol}) = 2.50 \times 10^{23} \text{ molecules SO}_2$

$SO_2 = 64.1 \text{ g/mol}$

$(0.414 \text{ mol})(64.1 \text{ g/mol}) = 26.5 \text{ g SO}_2$

2. Assume 100 g of the compound.

$\text{mol Ba} = \frac{62.62 \text{ g}}{137.3 \text{ g/mol}} = 0.456 \text{ mol Ba}$

$\text{mol As} = \frac{22.78 \text{ g As}}{74.9 \text{ g/mol}} = 0.304 \text{ mol As}$

$\text{mol O} = \frac{14.60 \text{ g}}{16.0 \text{ g/mol}} = 0.912 \text{ mol O}$

$\text{Formula} = Ba_{0.456}As_{0.304}O_{0.912}$

Dividing all subscripts by 0.304, we obtain a formula of $Ba_{1.5}AsO_3$. Since we have a fractional subscript, multiply all subscripts by 2 to obtain an empirical formula of $Ba_3As_2O_6$.

3. $2K_2CrO_4 + 6NaCl + 16HClO_4 \rightarrow 3Cl_2(g) + 2Cr(ClO_4)_3 + 6NaClO_4 + 4KClO_4 + 8H_2O + 277 \text{ kJ}$

A. $Cr(ClO_4)_3 = 52.0 + 3(35.5) + 12(16.0) = 350.5 \text{ g/mol}$

$(22.35 \text{ g})/(350.5 \text{ g/mol}) = 0.0638 \text{ mol Cr(ClO}_4)_3$

$[0.0638 \text{ mol Cr(ClO}_4)_3](\frac{16 \text{ mol HClO}_4}{2 \text{ mol Cr(ClO}_4)_3}) = 0.510 \text{ mol HClO}_4$

$HClO_4 = 100.5 \text{ g/mol}$

$(0.510 \text{ mol})(100.5 \text{ g/mol}) = 51.3 \text{ g HClO}_4$

B. $\frac{8.22 \text{ g H}_2\text{O}}{18.0 \text{ g/mol}} = 0.457 \text{ mol H}_2\text{O}$

$(0.457 \text{ mol H}_2\text{O})(\frac{3 \text{ mol Cl}_2}{8 \text{ mol H}_2\text{O}}) = 0.171 \text{ mol Cl}_2$

$(0.171 \text{ mol})(22.414 \text{ L/mol}) = 3.83 \text{ L Cl}_2$

C. $(132 \text{ kJ})(\frac{8 \text{ mol H}_2\text{O}}{277 \text{ kJ}}) = 3.81 \text{ mol H}_2\text{O}$

$(3.81 \text{ mol H}_2\text{O})(6.02 \times 10^{23} \text{ molecules/mol}) = 2.29 \times 10^{24} \text{ molecules H}_2\text{O}$

D. $(8.26 \times 10^{21} \text{ formula units NaCl})(\frac{16 \text{ molecules HClO}_4}{6 \text{ formula units NaCl}}) = 2.20 \times 10^{22} \text{ formula units NaCl}$

E. i. $K_2CrO_4 = 194.2 \text{ g/mol}$
$NaCl = 58.5 \text{ g/mol}$

$\frac{235.0 \text{ g K}_2\text{CrO}_4}{194.1 \text{ g/mol}} = 1.21 \text{ mol K}_2\text{CrO}_4$

$\frac{1.21 \text{ mol K}_2\text{CrO}_4}{2 \text{ mol K}_2\text{CrO}_4/\text{reaction}} = 0.605x$ (i.e., I have enough K_2CrO_4 to run the reaction 0.605 times.)

$\frac{235 \text{ g NaCl}}{58.5 \text{ g/mol}} = 4.02 \text{ mol NaCl}$

$\frac{4.02 \text{ mol NaCl}}{6 \text{ mol NaCl/reaction}} = 0.67x$ (i.e., I have enough NaCl to run the reaction 0.67 times.)

Therefore, K_2CrO_4 is the limiting reactant.

ii. $(1.21 \text{ mol } K_2CrO_4)(\frac{6 \text{ mol } NaClO_4}{2 \text{ mol } K_2CrO_4}) = 3.63 \text{ mol } NaClO_4$

$NaClO_4 = 122.5 \text{ g/mol}$

$(3.63 \text{ mol})(122.5 \text{ g/mol}) = 444.7 \text{ g } NaClO_4$

iii. mol NaCl consumed $= (1.21 \text{ mol } K_2CrO_4)(\frac{6 \text{ mol } NaCl}{2 \text{ mol } K_2CrO_4}) = 3.63 \text{ mol } NaCl$

g NaCl consumed $= (3.63 \text{ mol})(58.5 \text{ g/mol}) = 212.4 \text{ g}$

g NaCl in excess $= 235.0 - 212.4 = 22.6 \text{ g}$

4. **A. i.** Left.

   ii. Concentrations of CO_2 and H_2O will decrease, and concentration of O_2 will increase. Concentration of C_6H_6 will decrease—it will increase as it shifts to the left but will not get back to its original value.

   iii. K will remain constant.

   B. i. Left

   ii. The concentrations of C_6H_6 and O_2 will increase and the concentrations of CO_2 and H_2O will decrease.

   iii. K will decrease.

   C. i. Right. It shifts in the direction where there are more gaseous molecules.

   ii. Amounts of C_6H_6 and O_2 will decrease, and amounts of CO_2 and H_2O will increase.

   iii. K will remain constant.

5. $Al(NO_3)_3 = 213.0 \text{ g/mol}$

   $\frac{48.28 \text{ g}}{213.0 \text{ g/mol}} = 0.213 \text{ mol}$

   $[Al(NO_3)_3] = \frac{0.213 \text{ mol}}{0.628 \text{ L}} = 0.339 \text{ M}$

   $Al(NO_3)_3(s) \leftrightarrow Al^{3+} + 3NO_3^-$

   $[Al^{3+}] = 0.339 \text{ M}$

   $[NO_3^-] = 3(0.339) = 1.02 \text{ M}$

6. $SO_2Cl_2(g) + 8HBr(aq) \rightarrow H_2S(g) + 2HCl(aq) + 4Br_2(l) + 2H_2O(l)$

   $\frac{7.33 \text{ L } SO_2Cl_2}{22.414 \text{ L/mol}} = 0.327 \text{ mol } SO_2Cl_2$

   $(0.327 \text{ mol } SO_2Cl_2)(\frac{8 \text{ mol } HBr}{1 \text{ mol } SO_2Cl_2}) = 2.62 \text{ mol } HBr$

   $\frac{2.62 \text{ mol } HBr}{3.50 \text{ mol } HBr/L} = 0.749 \text{ L} = 749 \text{ mL}$

7. $Ca_3(PO_4)_2(s) \leftrightarrow 3Ca^{2+}(aq) + 2PO_4^{3-}(aq)$

   A. Left. The $Ca(NO_3)_2$ dissolves completely to form Ca^{2+} and NO_3^-, which raises the concentration of the Ca^{2+}, causing the system to shift to the left to try and reduce this stress.

   B. The amount of $Ca_3(PO_4)_2$ will increase, but its concentration remains constant, since it is a pure solid. Both the amount and concentration of PO_4^{3-} will decrease. Both the amount and concentration of Ca^{2+} will show a net increase, since you will not be able to completely remove this concentration stress.

8. $HC_4H_7O_2 \leftrightarrow H^+ + C_4H_7O_2^-$, $K_a = 1.5 \times 10^{-5}$

$\quad\quad x \quad\quad\quad \rightarrow \quad x \quad\quad\quad x$

Let $x = $ mol/L $HC_4H_7O_2$ that ionize.

$K_a = \frac{[H^+][C_4H_7O_2^-]}{[HC_4H_7O_2]} = 1.5 \times 10^{-5}$

$\frac{(x)(x)}{0.44 - x} = 1.5 \times 10^{-5}$

Assume x is negligible compared to 0.44.

$\frac{(x)(x)}{0.44} = 1.5 \times 10^{-5}$

$x^2 = 6.6 \times 10^{-6}$

$x = 2.57 \times 10^{-3}$

$[H^+] = 2.57 \times 10^{-3}$ M

$[C_4H_7O_2^-] = 2.57 \times 10^{-3}$ M

$[HC_4H_7O_2] = 0.44$ M

$[H^+][OH^-] = 1.00 \times 10^{-14}$

$(2.57 \times 10^{-3})[OH^-] = 1.00 \times 10^{-14}$

$[OH^-] = \frac{1.00 \times 10^{-14}}{2.57 \times 10^{-3}} = 3.89 \times 10^{-12}$ M

$pH = -\log[H^+] = -\log(2.57 \times 10^{-3}) = -(-2.59) = 2.59$

$pH + pOH = 14$

$pOH = 14 - pH = 14 - 2.59 = 11.41$

%ionization $= \frac{2.57 \times 10^{-3}}{0.44} \times 100 = 0.58\%$

9. $MgF_2(s) \leftrightarrow Mg^{2+} + 2F^-$, $K_{sp} = 3.7 \times 10^{-8}$

$\quad\quad x \quad\quad\quad\quad x \quad\quad 0.666 + 2x \quad$ [where $x = $ mol/L MgF_2 that dissolve]

There are 2 sources of F^- in this problem. The $2x$ mol/L come from the MgF_2, but we must also include the F^- that comes from the KF, which is completely soluble: $KF(s) \leftrightarrow K^+ + F^-$. We get another 0.666 mol/L F^- from the KF, so the total concentration of F^- is equal to $0.666 + 2x$.

$[Mg^{2+}][F^-]^2 = 3.7 \times 10^{-8}$

$(x)(0.666 + 2x)^2 = 3.7 \times 10^{-8}$

Assume $2x$ is negligible compared to 0.666.

$(x)(0.666)^2 = 3.7 \times 10^{-8}$

$x = \frac{3.7 \times 10^{-8}}{(0.666)^2} = 8.34 \times 10^{-8}$ M

So we can dissolve 8.34×10^{-8} mol/L of MgF_2.

mol $MgF_2 = (8.34 \times 10^{-8}$ mol/L$)(0.250$ L$) = 2.09 \times 10^{-8}$ mol

$MgF_2 = 62.3$ g/mol

g $MgF_2 = (2.09 \times 10^{-8}$ mol$)(62.3$ g/mol$) = 1.30 \times 10^{-6}$ g MgF_2

10. $Ba(IO_3)_2(s) \leftrightarrow Ba^{2+} + 2IO_3^-$

$$\quad\quad\quad\quad x \quad\quad x \quad\quad 2x \quad\quad\quad \text{[where } x = \text{mol/L } Ba(IO_3)_2 \text{ that dissolve]}$$

$[Ba^{2+}][IO_3^-]^2 = 1.5 \times 10^{-9}$

$(x)(2x)^2 = 1.5 \times 10^{-9}$

$(x)(4x^2) = 1.5 \times 10^{-9}$

$4x^3 = 1.5 \times 10^{-9}$

$x^3 = 3.75 \times 10^{-10}$

$x = 7.2 \times 10^{-4}$

So molar solubility = 7.2×10^{-4} M.

11. $2A + B \leftrightarrow C + 3D$

$K = \frac{[C][D]^3}{[A]^2[B]}$

The real problem is to find the equilibrium concentrations of all 3 substances, which is really a stoichiometry problem.

[C] = 0.38 M (given)

[D] = 3(0.38) = 1.14 M

For A and B, you must subtract what is consumed from what you started with to find their equilibrium concentrations.

[A] = 1.30 − 2(0.38) = 0.54 M

[B] = 2.20 − 0.38 = 1.82 M

$K = \frac{(0.38)(1.14)^3}{(0.54)^2(1.82)} = 1.07$

12. $A + 3B \leftrightarrow 2C + D$

$K = \frac{[C]^2[D]}{[A][B]^3}$

Again, the real problem is to find the equilibrium concentrations. We need to find out how much A is consumed. This will allow us to determine how much C and D are formed and how much B is consumed.

mol A consumed = initial mol − final (equilibrium) mol = 1.75 − 1.26 = 0.49 mol/L

Now let's find all of the equilibrium concentrations.

[A] = 1.26 M (given)

[B] = 2.75 − 3(0.49) = 1.28 M

[C] = 0.65 + 2(0.49) = 1.63 M

[D] = 0.49 M

$K = \frac{(1.63)^2(0.49)}{(1.26)(1.28)^3} = 0.49$

Wow! It came out to be the same number as the number of moles per liter of A consumed! Was there a reason for that? No, it truly was just a coincidence.

13. A. 56 protons, 54 electrons, 81 neutrons

    B. 52 protons, 54 electrons, 76 neutrons

    C. 98 protons, 98 electrons, 153 neutrons

14. A. Noble gases

    B. Alkali metals

    C. Halogens

    D. Alkaline earth metals

    E. Chalcogens

15. $(7.00 \text{ mL})(13.6 \text{ g/mL}) = 95.2 \text{ g Hg}$

$$\frac{95.2 \text{ g}}{200.6 \text{ g/mol}} = 0.475 \text{ mol}$$

$(0.475 \text{ mol})(6.02 \times 10^{23} \text{ atoms/mol}) = 2.86 \times 10^{23} \text{ atoms Hg}$

16. A. $Ca_3(PO_4)_2 + 3SiO_2 \leftrightarrow P_2O_5 + 3CaSiO_3$

    B. $4CuCl + O_2 + 4HCl \leftrightarrow 4CuCl_2 + 2H_2O$

    C. $2B_2O_3 + 7C \leftrightarrow B_4C + 6CO$

    D. $4H_3N + 3O_2 \leftrightarrow 2N_2 + 6H_2O$

    E. $3NO_2 + H_2O \leftrightarrow 2HNO_3 + NO$

    F. $6NaOH + 3Cl_2 \leftrightarrow NaClO_3 + 5NaCl + 3H_2O$

17. $NaOH = 40.0 \text{ g/mol}$

$(7.83 \text{ g})/(40.0 \text{ g/mol}) = 0.196 \text{ mol}$

$$\frac{0.196 \text{ mol}}{0.72 \text{ mol/L}} = 0.272 \text{ L} = 272 \text{ mL}$$

18. $3SnCl_4(aq) + 4K_3PO_4(aq) \rightarrow 12KCl(aq) + Sn_3(PO_4)_4(s)$

    A. $\text{mol SnCl}_4 = (0.225 \text{ L})(1.85 \text{ mol/L}) = 0.4162 \text{ mol SnCl}_4$

        $\frac{0.4162 \text{ mol}}{3 \text{ mol/reaction}} = 0.1387x$ (i.e., I have enough $SnCl_4$ to run the reaction 0.1387 times.)

        $\text{mol K}_3PO_4 = (0.350 \text{ L})(1.77 \text{ mol/L}) = 0.6195 \text{ mol K}_3PO_4$

        $\frac{0.6195 \text{ mol}}{4 \text{ mol/reaction}} = 0.1549x$ (i.e., I have enough K_3PO_4 to run the reaction 0.1549 times.)

    $SnCl_4$ is the limiting reactant.

    B. $Sn_3(PO_4)_4 = 3(118.7) + 4(31.0) + 16(16.0) = 736.1 \text{ g/mol}$

        $(0.4162 \text{ mol SnCl}_4)(\frac{1 \text{ mol Sn}_2(PO_4)_4}{3 \text{ mol SnCl}_4}) = 0.1387 \text{ mol Sn}_3(PO_4)_4$

        $[0.1387 \text{ mol Sn}_3(PO_4)_4](736.1 \text{ g/mol}) = 102 \text{ g Sn}_3(PO_4)_4$

Periodic Table of Elements

1 H																	2 He
3 Li	4 Be											5 B	6 C	7 N	8 O	9 F	10 Ne
11 Na	12 Mg											13 Al	14 Si	15 P	16 S	17 Cl	18 Ar
19 K	20 Ca	21 Sc	22 Ti	23 V	24 Cr	25 Mn	26 Fe	27 Co	28 Ni	29 Cu	30 Zn	31 Ga	32 Ge	33 As	34 Se	35 Br	36 Kr
37 Rb	38 Sr	39 Y	40 Zr	41 Nb	42 Mo	43 Tc	44 Ru	45 Rh	46 Pd	47 Ag	48 Cd	49 In	50 Sn	51 Sb	52 Te	53 I	54 Xe
55 Cs	56 Ba	57 La	72 Hf	73 Ta	74 W	75 Re	76 Os	77 Ir	78 Pt	79 Au	80 Hg	81 Tl	82 Pb	83 Bi	84 Po	85 At	86 Rn
87 Fr	88 Ra	89 Ac	104 Rf	105 Db	106 Sg	107 Bh	108 Hs	109 Mt	110 Ds	111 Rg							

58 Ce	59 Pr	60 Nd	61 Pm	62 Sm	63 Eu	64 Gd	65 Tb	66 Dy	67 Ho	68 Er	69 Tm	70 Yb	71 Lu
90 Th	91 Pa	92 U	93 Np	94 Pu	95 Am	96 Cm	97 Bk	98 Cf	99 Es	100 Fm	101 Md	102 No	103 Lr

Appendices

SI Base Units

Measurement	Unit	Symbol
Length	meter	m
Mass	kilogram	kg
Time	second	s
Temperature	Kelvin	K
Amount of substance	mole	mol
Electric current	ampere	A
Luminous intensity	candela	cd

SI Prefixes

Multiple	Prefix	Symbol
10^{24}	yotta	Y
10^{21}	zetta	Z
10^{18}	exa	E
10^{15}	peta	P
10^{12}	tera	T
10^{9}	giga	G
10^{6}	mega	M
10^{3}	kilo	k
10^{2}	hecto	h
10^{1}	deka	da
10^{0}		
10^{-1}	deci	d
10^{-2}	centi	c
10^{-3}	milli	m
10^{-6}	micro	μ
10^{-9}	nano	n
10^{-12}	pico	p
10^{-15}	femto	f
10^{-18}	atto	a
10^{-21}	zepto	z
10^{-24}	yocto	y

Formulas

Topic	Equation
Density	$D = \dfrac{mass}{volume}$
Molarity	$M = \dfrac{moles\ solute}{liters\ solution}$
Chemical equilibrium	$w\text{A} + x\text{B} \leftrightarrow y\text{C} + z\text{D}$ $K = \dfrac{[C]^y [D]^z}{[A]^w [B]^x}$
Self-ionization of water	$K_w = [\text{H}^+][\text{OH}^-] = 1.00 \times 10^{-14}$
Acids and bases	$\text{pH} = -\log [\text{H}^+]$ $\text{pOH} = -\log [\text{OH}^-]$ $\text{pH} + \text{pOH} = 14$ $\text{p}K_a = -\log K_a$

Common Monatomic Cations and Anions

Cations		Anions	
+1 Ions		−1 Ions	
Cesium	Cs^+	Bromide	Br^-
Copper(I) [cuprous]	Cu^+	Chloride	Cl^-
Hydrogen	H^+	Fluoride	F^-
Lithium	Li^+	Iodide	I^-
Potassium	K^+		
Rubidium	Rb^+		
Silver	Ag^+		
Sodium	Na^+		
+2 Ions		−2 Ions	
Barium	Ba^{2+}	Oxide	O^{2-}
Calcium	Ca^{2+}	Sulfide	S^{2-}
Chromium(II) [chromous]	Cr^{2+}		
Copper(II) [cupric]	Cu^{2+}		
Iron(II) [ferrous]	Fe^{2+}		
Lead(II) [plumbous]	Pb^{2+}		
Magnesium	Mg^{2+}		
Manganese(II) [manganous]	Mn^{2+}		
Mercury(I) [mercurous]	Hg_2^{2+}		
Mercury(II) [mercuric]	Hg^{2+}		
Nickel	Ni^{2+}		
Radium	Ra^{2+}		
Strontium	Sr^{2+}		
Tin(II) [stannous]	Sn^{2+}		
Zinc	Zn^{2+}		
+3 Ions		−3 Ions	
Aluminum	Al^{3+}	Nitride	N^{3-}
Bismuth	Bi^{3+}	Phosphide	P^{3-}
Chromium(III) [chromic]	Cr^{3+}		
Iron(III) [ferric]	Fe^{3+}		
+4 Ions			
Lead(IV) [plumbic]	Pb^{4+}		
Tin(IV) [stannic]	Sn^{4+}		

Common Polyatomic Ions

Name	Symbol
Acetate	$C_2H_3O_2^-$
Ammonium	NH_4^+
Arsenate	AsO_4^-
Carbonate	CO_3^{2-}
Chlorate	ClO_3^-
Chlorite	ClO_2^-
Chromate	CrO_4^{2-}
Cyanide	CN^-
Dichromate	$Cr_2O_7^{2-}$
Hydrogen sulfate	HSO_4^-
Hydronium	H_3O^+
Hydroxide	OH^-
Hypobromite	BrO_3^-
Hypochlorite	ClO^-
Iodate	IO_3^-
Nitrate	NO_3^-
Nitrite	NO_2^-
Perchlorate	ClO_4^-
Phosphate	PO_4^{3-}
Sulfate	SO_4^{2-}
Sulfite	SO_3^{2-}

Ionization Constants (at 298 K)

Not Acid or Base	Formula	Constant (K_w)
Water	H_2O	1.00×10^{-14}
Acid	**Formula**	**Constant (K_a)**
Acetic	$HC_2H_3O_2$	1.8×10^{-5}
Cyanic	$HOCN$	3.5×10^{-4}
Hydriodic	HI	∞
Hydrobromic	HBr	∞
Hydrochloric	HCl	∞
Hydrocyanic	HCN	4.9×10^{-10}
Hydrofluoric	HF	6.8×10^{-4}
Hydrogen sulfate ion	HSO_4^-	1.1×10^{-2}
Hypobromous	$HBrO$	2.5×10^{-9}
Hypochlorous	$HClO$	3.5×10^{-8}
Nitric	HNO_3	∞
Nitrous	HNO_2	4.5×10^{-4}
Perchloric	$HClO_4$	∞
Sulfuric	H_2SO_4	∞
Base	**Formula**	**Constant (K_b)**
Ammonia	NH_3	1.8×10^{-5}

Solubility Product Constants (at 298 K)

Compound	Formula	Constant (K_{sp})
Aluminum hydroxide	$Al(OH)_3$	1.3×10^{-33}
Barium sulfate	$BaSO_4$	1.1×10^{-10}
Bismuth sulfide	Bi_2S_3	1×10^{-97}
Calcium carbonate	$CaCO_3$	2.8×10^{-9}
Calcium fluoride	CaF_2	3.9×10^{-11}
Calcium hydroxide	$Ca(OH)_2$	5.5×10^{-6}
Calcium phosphate	$Ca_3(PO_4)_2$	1.1×10^{-26}
Copper(II) chromate	$CuCrO_4$	3.6×10^{-6}
Iron(III) hydroxide	$Fe(OH)_3$	4×10^{-38}
Lead chromate	$PbCrO_4$	2.8×10^{-13}
Lead sulfate	$PbSO_4$	1.6×10^{-8}
Lithium phosphate	Li_3PO_4	3.2×10^{-9}
Magnesium fluoride	MgF_2	3.7×10^{-8}
Magnesium hydroxide	$Mg(OH)_2$	1.8×10^{-11}
Magnesium phosphate	$Mg_3(PO_4)_2$	1×10^{-25}
Silver carbonate	Ag_2CO_3	8.1×10^{-12}
Silver chloride	$AgCl$	1.8×10^{-10}
Strontium arsenate	$Sr_3(AsO_4)_2$	4.3×10^{-19}

Note: Roman numerals after the symbol of a metallic ion designate its charge [e.g., copper(II) = Cu^{2+} and iron(III) = Fe^{3+}].

Glossary

alkali metals: Elements in the first column of the periodic table, consisting of Li, Na, K, Rb, Cs, and Fr.

alkaline earth metals: Elements in the second column of the periodic table, consisting of Be, Mg, Ca, Sr. Ba, and Ra.

anion: A negatively charged ion.

atom: The fundamental particle that makes up an element. Atoms are made of a very small nucleus that contains protons and neutrons, surrounded by a cloud of electrons that reside outside the nucleus.

atomic mass unit: A very small unit of mass equal to $\frac{1}{12}$ the mass of a ^{12}C atom. It is also called a Dalton.

atomic number: A number that is equal to the number of protons in the nucleus of an atom or the number of electrons in a neutral atom.

atomic weight: The average weight of all the isotopes of an element.

Avogadro's hypothesis: At the same conditions of temperature and pressure, equal volumes of different gases contain the same number of molecules.

Avogadro's number: The number of particles in a mole, approximately equal to 6.02×10^{23}.

base units: The 7 fundamental units in the International System of Units (SI, or the metric system), from which all other units can be derived. The 7 base units are the meter, kilogram, second, Kelvin, mole, ampere, and candela.

cation: A positively charged ion.

chalcogens: The column of elements in the periodic table consisting of O, S, Se, Te, and Po.

chemical equilibrium: The state of a chemical reaction in which forward and reverse reactions are occurring at equal and opposite rates, so that the concentrations of substances present in the system do not change with time.

chemical reaction: A process in which one or more substances is transformed into one or more different substances.

conceptual definition: A definition expressed in such a way that it gets to the basic reason why something belongs to a particular set of things. These kinds of definitions tend to allow you to understand why something belongs to the set of things being defined, rather than allowing you to actually experimentally determine whether something belongs in that set of things.

cubic centimeter (abbr. **cm^3**): A relatively small unit of volume equal to the volume occupied by a cube 1 cm on a side.

density: A ratio of the amount of matter to the volume that it occupies, often expressed in grams per cubic centimeter (g/cm^3), although the proper SI unit is kilograms per cubic meter (kg/m^3).

derived units: All SI units other than the 7 base units.

dissociation constant: *See* **ionization constant**.

electron: A negatively charged fundamental particle that exists outside the nucleus of an atom.

element: Operationally, a substance that cannot be broken down into simpler substances by ordinary physical and chemical techniques. Conceptually, it is a substance that is made of only one kind of atom.

empirical formula: The formula of a compound written with the lowest possible whole-number ratio of the atoms of the elements in the compound.

English system: The measurement system commonly used in the United States, consisting of units such as inches, feet, yards, miles, pints, quarts, gallons, pounds, and ounces.

equilibrium: *See* **chemical equilibrium**.

equilibrium constant: The numerical value obtained when the equilibrium concentrations of the reactants and products are substituted into the equilibrium constant expression.

equilibrium constant expression: The expression obtained by multiplying the concentrations of the products and then dividing by the multiplied concentrations of the reactants, with each concentration having been raised to a power equal to the coefficient of that substance in the balanced chemical equation.

equivalence point: The point in a titration where the acid and base have been mixed in the proper mole ratio to just neutralize each other.

factor-label method: A conversion process by which the quantity being converted is multiplied by a conversion factor (fraction) with units in the appropriate place (numerator/denominator). This process is also referred to as dimensional analysis or the unit factor method.

formula unit: One empirical formula of an ionic solid.

gram: A unit of mass equal to the mass of 1 cm^3 of water at its point of maximum density, which occurs at a temperature of about $4°C$.

halogens: The next-to-last column of elements in the periodic table, consisting of the elements F, Cl, Br, I, and At.

HONClBrIF: A mnemonic device for remembering the diatomic elements. It is pronounced "hon-kil-brif."

inner transition elements: The 2 rows of elements typically placed at the bottom of most periodic tables and separated from the rest of the table.

ion: A charged particle formed when an atom or group of atoms has gained or lost one or more electrons.

ionic compound: A compound that consists of positively and negatively charged ions held together by electrostatic attraction.

ionization constant: An equilibrium constant for the dissociation of an acid, a base, or water into ionized components.

isotopes: Atoms of the same element that differ in the number of neutrons in their nuclei.

joule: The SI unit of energy.

Kelvin: The SI base unit for temperature.

kilogram: The SI base unit for mass.

Le Chatelier's principle: If a stress is applied to a system at equilibrium, the system will shift, if possible, in the direction that completely (or at least partially) alleviates the stress.

limiting reactant (a.k.a. **limiting reagent**): The reactant in a chemical reaction that will limit the amount of product that can be produced.

mass: The amount of matter something contains.

mass number: A number that is equal to the total number of protons and neutrons in the nucleus of particular atom and/or the mass of that isotope rounded off to the nearest whole number.

metal: An element that generally will have the properties of being shiny when its surface is polished, being malleable, being ductile, and being a good conductor of heat and electricity; it will tend to form positive ions when taking part in a chemical reaction.

metalloids (a.k.a. **semimetals**): Elements located near the staircase-like line that separates metals from nonmetals in the periodic table. Metalloids exhibit properties of both metals and nonmetals.

meter: One of the 7 SI base units of measurement. It is equal to the distance that light travels in a vacuum in $\frac{1}{299,792,458}$ s.

milliliter (abbr. **mL**): A relatively small unit of volume equal in size to a cubic centimeter (cm^3).

molar mass: The mass of 1 mol of a substance.

molar volume: The volume or space occupied by 1 mol of a substance. At STP, 1 mol of any gas occupies a volume of 22.414 L.

molarity: The number of moles of solute divided by the total number of liters of solution in which this amount of solute is dissolved; denoted by the symbol M.

mole: One of the 7 SI base units of measurement. Its formal definition is that it is a number equal to the number of carbon atoms in exactly 12 g of ^{12}C. This number, called Avogadro's number, is equal to approximately 6.02214×10^{23} (usually rounded to 6.02×10^{23}). In practical terms, 1 mol of a substance is equal to the atomic, molecular, or formula weight of the substance expressed in grams.

molecule: A particle made by combining 2 or more atoms.

neutron: An electrically neutral particle in the nucleus of an atom.

noble gases: The last column in the periodic table, consisting of the elements He, Ne, Ar, Kr, Xe, and Rn.

nonmetal: An element whose properties are opposite to those of a metal. Nonmetals tend to be dull, brittle, poor conductors of heat and electricity, and they tend to gain electrons when they form ions.

operational definition: A definition expressed in such a way that one can perform the operation(s) described in the definition to determine if something actually fits the definition and should be considered to be a member of the set of things being described.

percent composition: The composition of a compound expressed as the percent mass of each element in the compound.

periodic table: An arrangement of the elements into chemical groups or families.

polyatomic ion: An ion containing more than 1 atom.

proton: A positively charged fundamental particle in the nucleus of an atom.

representative elements: The first 2 and last 6 columns of elements in the periodic table.

SI: The international metric system of units. The abbreviation comes from the French: *Système international d'unités*.

solubility equilibria: The kind of equilibria that exist in saturated solutions of ionic solids.

stoichiometry: The area of chemistry that deals with the relationships between the amounts of substances involved in a chemical reaction.

STP: An abbreviation for "standard temperature and pressure," which are defined as 273 K (0°C) and 1 atmosphere of pressure.

strong acid or base: An acid or base that is highly ionized in aqueous solution, typically close to or equal to 100%.

this per that: A quotient that specifies how much you have of whatever is in the numerator for 1 of whatever is in the denominator, even if a number other than 1 actually appears on the denominator. The quotient can be divided out if you desire to actually have the denominator be the number 1.

titration: A laboratory procedure used to determine the concentration of some unknown solution (often of an acid or base).

transition elements: The rows of 10 elements, all metals, in the middle of the periodic table.

volume: The amount of space something occupies.

weak acid or base: An acid or base that is only slightly ionized in aqueous solution.

weight: A measure of the gravitational force of attraction being exerted on something.

Bibliography

Textbooks

One major problem with high school textbooks (and textbooks in general) is their expense, which usually will be considerably greater than the cost of this entire Teaching Company course. Another somewhat more subtle problem is that there is a strong tendency to stay with what has proven to sell in the past, a fact that often makes all the texts very similar to each other in content and style. In particular, as far as I have been able to determine, all texts use the factor-label approach to solving problems, since this is an approach that is easily and "clearly" presented and obviously works, at least in the short term. This is an approach I have recommended that you not rely on, although learning it and using it as a check on your reasoning is something that has value.

I've perused many (but not all) of the commonly used high school chemistry texts. None of them stand out from the rest as being significantly better or more useful. But there are a few choices that I can at least suggest as being appropriate for the majority of students taking a first-year high school chemistry course.

Bishop, Mark. *An Introduction to Chemistry*. http://preparatorychemistry.com. This is clearly written, nicely illustrated, and most importantly is both reasonably priced and can be downloaded from the Internet with only a shareware payment requested—but not required. Unfortunately, there are also significant gaps in the content coverage (particularly those connected to equilibria, both general and specific) that prevent me from recommending it overall. For other topics, however, it may prove useful.

Davis, Raymond E., Regina Frey, Mickey Sarquis, and Jerry L. Sarquis. *Modern Chemistry*. Orlando, FL: Holt, Rinehart, and Winston, 2009. This is one of the standard textbooks that is widely used and has been around for a very long time. I have a very high regard for one of the authors, with whom I have worked in the past on unrelated projects. Whatever the edition, it is a textbook that almost certainly is a sound and safe choice, although like many texts, its approach to problem solving is perhaps too mechanical. Additional information and study materials can be obtained at http://go.hrw.com/hrw.nd/gohrw_rls1/pKeywordResults?HC6%20STUDENT.

General Chemistry. http://en.wikibooks.org/wiki/General_Chemistry. Coverage in this free WikiBook, in my opinion, was not always that thorough, at least as of 2009.

Wilbraham, Antony C., Dennis D. Staley, Michael S. Matta, and Edward L. Waterman. *Prentice Hall Chemistry*. Upper Saddle River, NJ: Pearson Prentice Hall, 2007. This is a traditional text from a major publisher. While not significantly different from other traditional texts, I liked it a bit more than most. It has excellent visuals and contains a large number of interesting connections between chemistry and the "real world." I thought it emphasized concepts to a greater extent than most texts. For example, the section on density begins with the statement, "Perhaps someone has tricked you with this question, 'Which is heavier, a pound of lead or a pound of feathers?'" It does, unfortunately, slightly misstate Le Chatelier's principle, and it is weak on solubility product problems and the common ion effect, but these weaknesses are common in other high school texts as well.

Websites

There obviously is an incredible amount of information that can be accessed on the Internet. Taking term from a lecture, such as stoichiometry, acids and bases, pH, solubility equilibria, balancing equations, etc., will result in anywhere from several thousand to several million hits. The problem, sometimes, is that websites vary greatly in both their overall quality and accuracy; in addition, a website that is here today may be gone tomorrow.

That said, some of the more useful links that you might want to take a look at include the following.

Balancing Chemical Equations. http://www.chemistry-drills.com/balance.html. This site offers hundreds of trivial, easy, intermediate, and expert problems for practice balancing equations. Note that this page also includes links to sites that I do not recommend regarding stoichiometry.

General Chemistry Online! http://antoine.frostburg.edu/chem/senese/101/index.shtml. This site includes tutorials, a searchable glossary, answers and hints for 400 frequently asked questions, simulations, and an exam survival guide.

General Chemistry Starting Points for Students. http://www.chem1.com/chemed/genchem.shtml. This is a multipurpose site with numerous links to other sites. Most of the links connect to sites that are not particularly useful for high school students, but some may prove valuable. For example, the section on acids and bases (under "Tutorials by Topic") has links that might prove useful. The value of a particular site may depend on the academic level of the course you are taking and your particular style of approaching problem solving and learning.

General Chemistry Virtual Textbook. http://www.chem1.com/acad/webtext/virtualtextbook.html. Perhaps too comprehensive and aimed at a college general chemistry course, this site still has many relevant and useful links.

Story Problems. http://www.av8n.com/physics/ill-posed.htm. This really will not provide much specific help with the course, but I love the problem-solving philosophy espoused here, as well as many of the specific problems presented. Just kind of a fun site.

Experiments

Any laboratory activity, no matter how benign, always involves some small risk. An activity as simple as boiling water can result in an accident. Always follow directions when performing any activity you might find useful and educational, and any home experiment should be performed with adult supervision.

If you are enrolled in a high school course, your laboratory manual should probably serve as the foundation for your laboratory work. If you do not have access to a laboratory, the following references might prove beneficial.

Many home experiments are designed to be fun more than purely educational—not necessarily a bad thing, but not necessarily the best thing either. Choose whatever kinds of experiments appeal to you, hopefully some of both types.

Try to find experiments that directly relate to what was discussed in the lectures. I hesitate to recommend any particular website, as so many are available. My recommendation would be to use appropriate search words and then select those sites that appear to be most closely connected to your goals and needs. That said, a couple of sites that you might want to look at are as follows.

Chemistry Activities for Kids. http://chemistry.about.com/od/chemistryactivities/Chemistry_Activities_for_Kids.htm.

Chemistry Experiments for Kids. http://homeschooling.gomilpitas.com/directory/Chemistry.htm.

If you desire an actual book for chemistry experiments, here is one that you might consider.

Thompson, Robert Bruce. *Illustrated Guide to Home Chemistry Experiments.* Sebastopol, CA: O'Reilly Media, 2008.

Notes

Notes